Great Hometown Restaurants of Texas

Mary Frances Beverley

Lone Star Books
A Division of
Gulf Publishing Company
Houston, Texas

Dedication

To Jim Beverley

Acknowledgments

Special appreciation to those whose encouragement and cooperation contributed so greatly to this book: Louis Hochman, Ann Ruff, Gary James, W. H. "Buckshot" Price and the Texas Restaurant Association, and the Texas Tourist Development Agency. Also to the editors of *Texas Highways* and to the following chambers of commerce: Abilene, Amarillo, Beaumont, Corpus Christi, Dalhart, Del Rio, Denison, Denton, Euless, Fredericksburg, Galveston, Grand Prairie, Harlingen, Jefferson, Kerrville, Longview, Nacogdoches, New Braunfels, Palestine, Round Rock, San Angelo, San Antonio, San Marcos, Sonora, Texarkana, Tyler, Uvalde, and Waco.

Drawings by Irin Lewis
Cartography by David T. Price

Great Hometown Restaurants of Texas

Library of Congress Cataloging in Publication Data

Beverley, Mary Frances.
   Great hometown restaurants of Texas.
   Includes index.
   1. Restaurants, lunch rooms, etc.—Texas—Directories.
I. Title.
TX907.B48 1984   647′.95764   84-10007
ISBN 0-88415-390-8

Contents

Preface

Remember the last time you drove the interstate? For ten miles your stomach had been signaling that it was lunch time. In the distance, tree tops and a water tower told you a town lay ahead. By the time you reached the flashing yellow light on the edge of town, you found yourself facing the old question: Which would it be, a consistent but boring fast food place, or would you get lucky and find that perfect little home-owned restaurant known only to the townsfolk and regular travelers along this route? How can you know for certain if a restaurant is going to be a serendipitous discovery to tell friends about? It's true that a lineup of assorted vehicles out front is one clue to a good restaurant: a smattering of pickups, a police car or two, one or two expensive cars, a city utility truck. Out-of-state licenses don't count. Those travelers may be just as unsure as you are.

In his book *Blue Highways*, author William Least Heat Moon describes his method of judging a restaurant as soon as he steps inside. Moon looks for wall calendars from local businesses. The more the better. They indicate that local businessmen eat there regularly. In addition, good evidence is several wall plaques representing the Lions Club, Toastmasters, etc., showing that local organizations have chosen that restaurant for their regular meeting place. Don't let the outside decor or lack of it discourage you. An old cafe with a screen door with three knots in the spring is bound to be a good place to eat. The owners have been so busy running the place, they simply haven't gotten around to putting on a new door.

Don't let *anyone* doubt the quality of Texas' home-owned restaurants. Only one hundred of the best are included in this book. I could have selected two hundred or three hundred! They were chosen according to the following criteria:

1. The restaurant is owned and operated by residents of the town.
2. The restaurant's success and popularity have been consistent for a number of years.
3. Every aspect of the restaurant is top quality: food (the type doesn't matter); decor (not necessarily elaborate but attractive and inviting); cleanliness; friendly, efficient employees; exceptionally good service.
4. The owner and/or manager shows conspicuous interest in the guests' enjoyment and satisfaction and is personally involved in the day-to-day operation of the restaurant.

Almost all the restaurants are located in the smaller towns and cities. Texas' big cities also have fine home-owned restaurants, but the restaurants listed in this book were selected, in addition to the criteria named, for their accessibility to the traveler, the tourist, and the newcomer to Texas. They are housed in buildings designed to be restaurants but also in old hotels and homes, old depots, cotton gins, grist mills, school houses, banks, and grocery stores. They range from family-style seating for country cooking, served in simple surroundings as at Allen's in Sweetwater, to gourmet dining amid Victorian elegance at the Durham House in Waxahachie.

Although the settings and menus vary, the most important common denominator of any successful restaurant does not. The independent restaurateur is one of the most energetic, hard-working, conscientious businesspersons there are (note that some of them are women). Many learned the business from their parents, working as youngsters in the family restaurant. Now their own families work as cooks, waiters, or cashiers, perhaps insuring that the home-owned restaurant is not going to disappear. Many of these restaurateurs belong to the Texas Restaurant Association, which annually honors its outstanding members (look for their plaques around restaurant cash registers). The organization promotes the highest standards of service, quality, and sanitation among its nearly six thousand members.

A few words about Texas' favorite dishes. Chili is the official state dish. If you aren't intimately acquainted with its pyrotechnic potential, don't ask a waiter if it's hot. "Not *that* hot" is the most innocent understatement ever made in a Texas restaurant. The same goes for any dish containing jalapeño peppers and for *salsa*, the spicy, often fiery sauce served in all Mexican restaurants. Some of them call theirs *pico de gallo*, which means *rooster beak*. That should give you the idea.

Recently, the subject of how to prepare and serve chicken fried steak has become as controversial as that of chili. I'm not taking sides, but you will be able to find good chicken fried steak in almost any home-owned restaurant in the state. Certainly it can stand right up there with the best Texas dishes—right there alongside Gulf shrimp, a ribeye, and barbecue. In almost every restaurant which serves it, it's the number one seller on the menu.

There are no "best" lists for food or restaurants in this book. Each one would be too long. In countless home-owned restaurants you can find great chili, chicken fried steak, and barbecue, and asking two people at the same time where to find the best will only start an argument. To find good barbecue, look for a place with a big woodpile nearby. It doesn't matter what kind of wood: mesquite, pecan, almost any hardwood. (The kind of wood is only part of the controversy over how to cook barbecue.)

Another popular, relatively new menu offering is calf and turkey fries. They're crunchy and tasty, but if you want to know more, ask the waitress or restaurant owner. If you're easily embarrassed, don't.

One writer has asked the wry question, "Is there food after Fort Stockton?" Indeed there is, and there are also wonderful restaurants in such places as Freer, Tulia, Blessing, Van, Sterling City, Hondo, and other small towns off the interstate and along the backroads. Go seek them out and discover for yourself the many great hometown restaurants of Texas.

Mary Frances Beverley

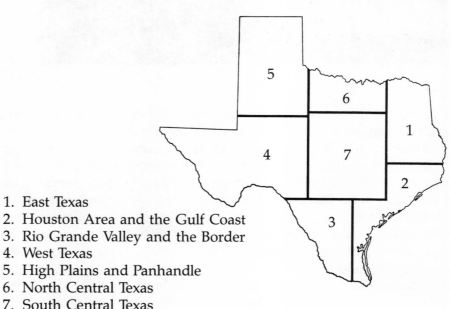

1. East Texas
2. Houston Area and the Gulf Coast
3. Rio Grande Valley and the Border
4. West Texas
5. High Plains and Panhandle
6. North Central Texas
7. South Central Texas

East Texas

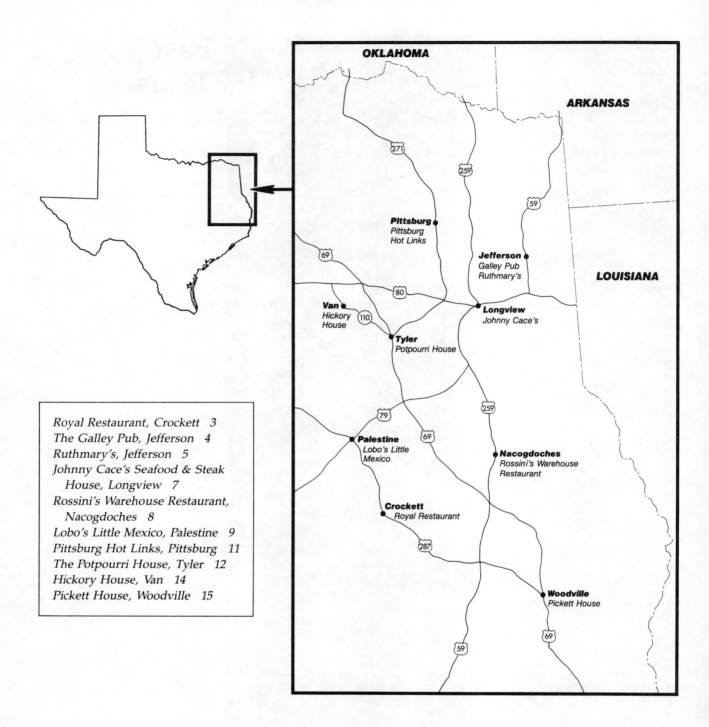

Any restaurant which has been in the same location, attracting both townspeople and travelers for over seventy years, is worth checking out. It doesn't take long to figure out the reason behind the Royal's longevity besides good food. It almost never closes—only on Christmas Day. That's right; it's open twenty-four hours a day and *only closes on Christmas Day.* If the Royal had been in business in 1836, Davy Crockett might have stopped in for a meal on his way to the Alamo instead of just camping nearby. A marvelous tile mural of the town's namesake is in one of the restaurant's dining rooms.

The noon buffet is one of the big attractions at the Royal. Homemade vegetable soup is seasoned with the hand of a chef who really knows Southern cooking. A typical buffet menu will include beef tips, chicken, okra, green beans, black-eyed peas, corn bread muffins, and banana pudding.

Meat for chili is ground in the kitchen, and owner Shroyer promises it is "not hot." (His regular guests say you can believe him.) The round steak used in chicken fried steak is also cut and trimmed on the premises and is one of the most frequently served menu items.

Service is snappy and efficient, and if you're in the mood for visiting with townsfolk, strike up a conversation with some at a nearby table. Crockett is such an old-fashioned friendly town, it still has a little grocery store that charges and delivers. With a spirit like that, eating in the town's oldest restaurant is sure to be an experience you'll enjoy and remember.

Serving hours: Twenty-four hours a day.
Closed: Christmas Day.
Breakfast, lunch, dinner, afternoon snacks.
Cost of average meal: Inexpensive to moderate.
Special plates and prices: Child's plate. Vegetable plate, one dollar less than the entree.
Credit cards accepted: Visa, MasterCard. Personal checks accepted.
Wheelchair accommodations: Front door and restrooms.
Parking: Limited.
No alcohol served.

Royal Restaurant

115 S. 5th Street, across from the courthouse
Crockett
(409) 544-3863
Owner: Nathan Shroyer

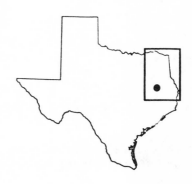

The Royal Restaurant is open twenty-four hours a day, every day of the year except Christmas Day.

The Galley Pub

121 W. Austin
Jefferson
(214) 665-3641
Owners: Lyle, Bonnie, Lyle, Jr.,
*   Becky, and Rosanne*
*   Spellings*

If you've ever wondered if there is a single Texas hamlet without the famous golden arches or the big red, horizontal teardrop or if it seems that a red-roofed building with a white bucket rotating on top always means you have reached civilization, cry no more. There is Jefferson. Jefferson—where the past hovers gently over gleaming white Victorian homes, surrounded by picket fences, baskets of fern hanging over wide porches, crepe myrtle blooming in the yards . . . and pine trees line Big Cypress Bayou where steamboats once churned into the state's primary inland port, and antique shops, grand old hotels, and restaurants are housed in lovingly restored structures from days long past.

The Galley Pub restaurant was the site of an odd melange of businesses and activities during the 1800s: a law practice, cock fighting, a Chinese laundry, and, upstairs, a bordello. Today, it serves as a tranquil setting for one of Jefferson's most popular restaurants.

The Galley Pub is housed in one of Jefferson's many historic structures.

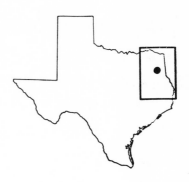

Enter at the side, and be greeted by one of the gracious Spellings family who are the present owners. They have designed a menu to suit any taste or appetite in your party. On a Saturday, their soup of the day will be offered, along with a wide selection of deli foods and salads. For a light lunch on a week day, you may want to try the marinated chicken breast or the hot shrimp with remoulade.

Among their "Not So Hungry" selections are some dishes sure to satisfy, even if you are more than "not so hungry." There is sauteed lump crab with mushrooms, Swiss cheese, and broccoli, served with a peach half, or the tasty Italian sandwich, the muffaletta, made with ham and Swiss cheese, and covered with an Italian sauce.

The crabmeat soup, served only at night, is a special favorite of regular diners. Entrees include ribeye steaks, fried oysters, and red snapper.

Anyone concerned about calories should not even read about the desserts listed on the menu. Creole bread pudding is served warm with whiskey sauce. "Sno-Pie" is a frozen dessert with pineapple, sour cream, coconut and rum, and "Strawberry Amaretto" combines fresh strawberries (in season) with Amaretto and whipped cream.

Serving hours: 11 a.m.–2 p.m., 5 p.m.–10 p.m. Tuesday through
   Saturday.
Closed: Sunday, Monday, New Year's Day and two or three days
   afterward, July Fourth, Thanksgiving, Christmas Eve, Christmas Day,
   New Year's Eve.
Lunch and dinner.
Cost of average meal: Inexpensive to moderate.
Credit cards accepted: American Express, Visa, MasterCard. Local
   personal checks accepted.
Special occasion services: Candle on one of the special desserts.
Wheelchair accommodations: Front door and restrooms.
Reservations requested on weekends.
Parking: Spacious.

Railroad magnate Jay Gould was seldom wrong. But in the 1800s, when Jefferson declined to cooperate in the building of his railroad through the town, he scrawled on one of the town's hotel registers "the end of Jefferson." Today, his private railroad car sits alongside one of the most graceful restaurants in Jefferson, and after a meal at Ruthmary's, you would enjoy a brief guided tour through the luxurious car.

Many of the stately homes in Jefferson date back to the mid-1800s. In 1920 or so a big white boarding house was built on Austin Street, and today the lower floor serves as Ruthmary's, now owned by its

Ruthmary's

210 Austin Street
Jefferson
(214) 665-8922
Owners: B. J. Russell and
*   Tracye Russell*

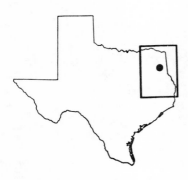

second mother-daughter team, B. J. Russell and daughter Tracye. Dining here, you will sense that time has stopped as you sit among gleaming period furniture, your table set with fine china, crystal, and old silverplate flatware. Soft music from the 1930s and 1940s blends with the feeling of timelessness.

The menu is posted daily on a chalkboard sign by the front picket fence. The primary evening entree is always prime rib with an alternative choice of a fish or chicken dish. Everything is elegantly prepared. The spinach salad and its house dressing are so good, visitors often ask for the dressing recipe. B. J. is generous enough to share it, so here it is:

1 cup vegetable oil	2 tablespoons sugar
5 tablespoons red wine vinegar	2 tablespoons chopped parsley
	2 cloves garlic, crushed
4 tablespoons sour cream	coarsely ground black pepper
1½ teaspoons salt	to taste
½ teaspoon dry mustard	

Whisk the ingredients together or shake in a bottle with a tight-fitting lid. This recipe makes enough for fifteen to twenty salads. The salad itself is always topped with a couple of purple onion rings and grated hard-boiled egg.

Ruthmary's warm, homemade rolls are wonderful as is the cornbread. Desserts, of course, follow the tradition of Southern ambrosial delights: Chantilly crepes containing vanilla pudding, bananas, whipped cream, and rum, and cheesecake with blueberries.

Wine and mixed drinks are available, one with the fanciful name of "Scarlett O," a combination of champagne and Amaretto.

Following your meal, you're welcome to sit on the big porch swing and watch other Jefferson visitors ride by in canopied surreys or stroll slowly past, which is the only way to enjoy and absorb Jefferson, the town where they have just almost stopped the clocks.

Serving hours: 11:30 a.m.–2 p.m. daily except Tuesday; 6:30 p.m. and 8 p.m. separate dinner seatings Monday, Friday, and Saturday.

Closed: Tuesday and Wednesday, Thanksgiving, mid-December through mid-February.

Lunch and dinner.

Cost of average meal: Moderate.

No credit cards accepted. Personal checks accepted.

Special occasion services: Candle on a dessert and a song.

Wheelchair accommodations: Front door.

Reservations requested for Friday, Saturday nights, and parties of ten or more.

Parking: Spacious.

Johnny Cace's Seafood & Steak House

1501 E. Marshall (U.S. Hwy. 80)
Longview
(214) 753-7691
Owners: John S. Cace, Jr., and Gerard C. Cace

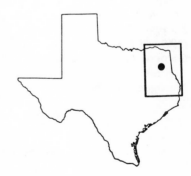

At Johnny Cace's, when you talk about tradition as the foundation for a top-notch restaurant, you're talking about Grandfather Cace's oyster beds in Louisiana; Johnny and Gerard who own the Longview restaurant; John III who operates the San Antonio branches; and Danny who manages the Tyler Cace's; along with employees who have been with the family businesses for as long as forty years; and Coleman, the oyster shucker, who has been performing his skill for fifteen years. Now, that's tradition!

For thirty-five years, seafood and steak lovers have been filling the 475-seat Longview restaurant to enjoy the freshest seafood available, including oysters which slept in their shells the night before you eat them, served in a variety of ways. There are "Oysters Rockefeller," of course, and also "Oysters Casino," which are fresh oysters on shell, baked with a cheese and wine sauce, mixed with herbs, and sprinkled with bacon chips. Shrimp gumbo is a favorite of returning diners, and shrimp also comes prepared in a number of tempting combinations: teamed with oysters, crab, or steak; fried; or in salads. Lobster, flounder, trout, catfish, and redfish are also served in delectable dishes.

All the steaks are aged at the restaurant, and they too are paired with a seafood selection, if you wish. One guest was heard to say, "We drive over from Dallas once a year as a special occasion just to eat here. But I always have such a hard time deciding what to have. I think about it all the way from Dallas!"

Not many restaurants' relish dishes are worthy of rhapsodizing over, but at Cace's you'll definitely be tempted to fill up before your meal arrives on cheddar cheese spread on toasted bread slices, pickled okra, corn relish, and bread and butter pickles. However, you won't have long to nibble because the service is fast and personal. With twenty-five to thirty years' experience serving Cace's guests, Ruby or Faye or one of the other nice waitresses will show you what experience and caring can mean.

An attractive separate menu for children lists fish and chicken dishes along with sandwiches, including grilled cheese and peanut butter and jelly. Now that's striving to please!

Of course the desserts are homemade and memorable: hot Dutch apple pie, black bottom pie, coconut cream or egg custard pie, and other sweet endings to your meal.

The San Antonio Cace-owned restaurants are The Bayous on Nacogdoches Road at I-410 and The Bayous Riverside on the River Walk. The newest Cace's is in Tyler at South Broadway and Thigpen.

Serving hours: 3 p.m.–10 p.m. Sunday and Monday; 11 a.m.–11 p.m. Tuesday, Wednesday and Thursday; 11 a.m.–12 p.m. Friday and Saturday.
Closed: Labor Day, Thanksgiving, and Christmas Day.
Lunch, dinner, and afternoon snacks.
Cost of average meal: Moderate.
Credit cards accepted: American Express, Visa, MasterCard, Diners Club, Carte Blanche. No personal checks accepted.
Special occasion services: Cake and singing for birthdays and anniversaries.
Wheelchair accommodations: Front door (ramp from parking lot).
Parking: Spacious.

Rossini's Warehouse Restaurant

211 Old Tyler Rd.
Nacogdoches
(409) 569-1489
Owners: Randall and Dianna Scott
Manager: Terri Fielding

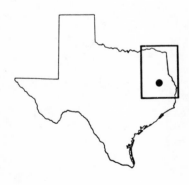

Nacogdoches claims to be the oldest town in Texas, and its many beautiful old homes, along with the Old Stone Fort built in the 1700s, and the quaint old depot, support that claim. Across the way from the depot, Rossini's occupies a grocery warehouse which was built in the early 1800s and used until it was converted into a restaurant in the 1970s. If you like the sound and vibrations of trains passing by, you'll love Rossini's because it sits so close to the tracks, you'll know it when a train rattles through town.

You won't be bothered by the train noises, however. (Trains aren't as common a sound as they were in Nacogdoches' early days, remember.) If you wish, you can eat in the room farthest from the tracks, which is the private club for the restaurant. A nice wine list is available as well as beer by the pitcher or a "Gimmydraw," which is Rossini's menuspeak for a glass of beer.

This may be the only restaurant in East Texas which doesn't serve chicken fried steak. Steaks are on the menu along with seafood, but the reason people flock to the restaurant is the Italian food. If you're alone, order spaghetti. As the menu reminds you, "No one is lonely while eating spaghetti. It requires too much attention!"

All the usual Italian dishes are prepared with conscientious attention to each. Both Veal Parmesan and Chicken Breast Cacciatora include spaghetti. Some meal-size sandwiches offered are "Fertita's Muffy," filled with ham, salami, Swiss, mozzarella, and American cheeses, black olives, green olives, onion, garlic, and celery. The "Stromboli" uses marinated pork tenderloin sauteed with onion and bell peppers and mozzarella cheese. An open-faced sandwich with

different toppings features an Italian bread drenched in garlic butter, then covered with cheese and/or sliced tomato and pepperoni.

Since owners Randall and Dianna Scott are both music major graduates from Stephen F. Austin State University in Nacogdoches, it isn't surprising to find live music and dancing many evenings at Rossini's.

Other attractions include special menu selections for children and a twenty percent discount for senior citizens and college students. If you appreciate antique furnishings and interesting old buildings, take time to walk around through all the downstairs rooms. You'll understand why Rossini's is such a special place in Nacogdoches where just about everyone wants to tell you about "the old warehouse restaurant down by the depot."

Serving hours: 11:30 a.m.–2 p.m. Monday through Sunday; 5 p.m.–10 p.m. Monday through Thursday; 5 p.m.–11 p.m. Friday and Saturday.
Closed: New Year's Day through January 3, July Fourth, Thanksgiving, Christmas Eve through December 29.
Lunch and dinner.
Cost of average meal: Inexpensive to moderate.
Credit cards accepted: American Express, Visa, MasterCard, Diners Club. No personal checks accepted.
Special occasion services: Entire staff helps celebrate all special occasions.
Wheelchair accommodations: Front door and restrooms.
Reservations requested for parties of eight or more.
Parking: Spacious.

As I visited the one hundred restaurants which appear in this book, I kept discovering several common denominators for a successful restaurant I hadn't been aware of before beginning my research. One is that at least one of the present owners is the son or daughter of a restaurant family. Another is when several members of the owner's family are involved in the restaurant operation. Most of today's owners such as these learned from their parents how to wait tables, wash dishes, cook, and how to treat their guests. Chip and Carolyn Wolfe are typical, with Carolyn as the one who grew up in a restaurant family. At Lobo's, almost anyone who greets you at the door, serves you, or prepares your food is apt to be related to Carolyn, Chip, or to both of them.

Lobo's is a family restaurant in other respects also. No alcohol is served nor permitted in the restaurant. A special child's Mexican

Lobo's Little Mexico

2027 W. Oak (U.S. Hwy. 79 W. at Loop 256)
Palestine
(214) 723-3143
Owners: Ernest (Chip) and Carolyn Wolfe

Lobo's is a family restaurant in more than one way—almost anyone who greets you at the door, serves you, or prepares your food is apt to be related to the owners.

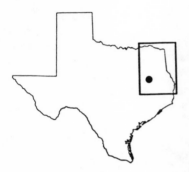

plate is available at a greatly reduced price. The atmosphere is friendly and relaxed.

No reservations are taken, but the restaurant is so popular, waiting lines are common. But the waiting room is comfortable, accommodating thirty people. Service is so good that you can expect a maximum of twenty minutes to wait.

The food is honest Tex-Mex, and the servings are the most generous you will have anywhere. Everyone has his own way of judging a menu's degree of freshness. With Mexican food, one measure is the quality of the avocados used in guacamole. Lobo's uses nothing but fresh Haas avocados, so you won't be disappointed. Try their nachos with guacamole, beans, cheese, jalapeños, and sour cream. Where the menu says "hot sauce," believe it. When the dinner you order includes chili, or if you order it a la carte, understand that this dish was not created for softies. After all, it's the official state dish and therefore must necessarily be spirited and attention-getting.

Freshness is the word that comes to mind no matter what you order at Lobo's. All foods that must be prepared from scratch, such as tortillas, are made fresh daily, and each order is individually prepared and oven-baked. Two kinds of made-fresh-daily pralines are available for a dessert.

A good sampling of Lobo's regular menu can be prepared to take out, but if you eat there, you will enjoy some of the snappiest service anywhere.

Serving hours: 11 a.m.–9:30 p.m. Tuesday through Saturday (11 a.m.–9 p.m. during DST months).
Closed: Sundays, Mondays, New Year's Day, July Fourth, Thanksgiving, Christmas Day.
Lunch and dinner.
Cost of average meal: Inexpensive.
No credit cards accepted. Personal checks accepted.
Special occasion services: Waitress will sing "Happy Birthday."
Wheelchair accommodations: Front door and restrooms.
Parking: Spacious.
No alcohol served.

One guidebook describes Pittsburg in terms of its production of peaches, vegetables, livestock, poultry, oil, gas, furniture, and bricks. There are surely some people with serious interests in these local products, but anyone who really understands what Pittsburg is all about knows that the major commodity of the little town is hot links! All-beef, German-style, spicy, greasy, messy, delicious hot links! And if dining niceties like tablecloths or place mats, good flatware, soft lighting, flowers on the table, or any other nonessential froufrou are important to you, forget about Pittsburg's.

But if you like the downhome basics of life, such as sitting down at a solid wooden table on a nice, sturdy bench and eating off of white butcher paper with only a plastic knife and fork, some hot sauce, and your favorite soft drink, you'll be happy here. Along with townsfolk in work clothes, others in shirts and ties, lots in jeans, and possibly even a fur-clad lady tourist, you can add to your hot links entree some green peppers, onions, pickles, and crackers, if you wish.

Pittsburg Hot Links

128 Marshall Street
Pittsburg
(214) 856-5765
Owner: Gene Warrick

You don't have to worry about how you're dressed in the casual surroundings of Pittsburg Hot Links.

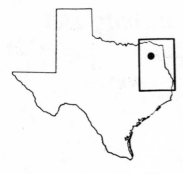

They're all available up at the counter where the friendly waitresses serve up as many links as you think you can hold. (The current record is 53.)

A German butcher named Charlie Hasselback started the hot links tradition in Pittsburg back in 1897. The present operation has been located in the same building since the 1930s. Owner Gene Warrick is the personification of the easy, laid-back attitude of East Texas. If you can't relax talking to Gene and eating his hot links, you'd better seek a long rest in total isolation. He likes to tell how he sends his links all over the country with special instructions to be sure to *bake* them. Somehow it's hard to imagine their tasting as good anywhere else except being eaten off butcher paper at his long wooden tables.

In Pittsburg they like to tell the story about the town's doctor a good many years back. Someone asked him how he happened to settle in Pittsburg. He replied, "I found out the fools here ate okra and hot links, so I knew my medical practice would do well." The doctor is no longer with us, but plenty of Pittsburg natives have grown up eating the famous hot links with no apparent ill effects. Probably eat okra, too.

Serving hours: 9 a.m.–6 p.m. Monday through Saturday.
Closed: Sundays, New Year's Day, July Fourth, Thanksgiving, Christmas Day.
Lunch and dinner.
Cost of average meal: Inexpensive.
No credit cards accepted. Personal checks accepted.
Wheelchair accommodations: Front door.
Parking: Limited.
No alcohol served.

The Potpourri House

308 W. Front and Bois d'Arc
Tyler
(214) 595-6782
Owners: Les and Carol
    Ellsworth

Lunch guests who appreciate English antiques will especially enjoy the setting for the Potpourri House. Three rooms of the early-century home have been filled with handsome old pieces and appealing reproductions. In fact, antique lovers may find it hard to concentrate on eating because of the surroundings. Once the homemade soup arrives, however, the fragrance of the tomato bouillon or cream of cauliflower will remind you why you came.

This is not a place only for ladies. All portions are generous enough for male appetites, too. The hot sandwiches, such as the "Turkey Noble Colossal," are a full meal. The "Turkey Noble" is breast of turkey, Swiss cheese, and bacon, served on an open-faced Kaiser roll covered with hot, bubbling cheese sauce. "Heavenly Chicken Salad" is crunchy with toasted almonds and green grapes and is served with

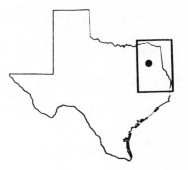

avocado and tomato wedges. An elaborate ham sandwich is offered for another cold meal for warm weather or for lighter appetites.

A daily special will tempt you with such choices as "Chicken Divan," white meat of chicken over broccoli with water chestnuts and sliced mushrooms. Or "Shrimp Potpourri," savory and steaming over fresh mushrooms and artichoke hearts. Fresh-baked breads with butter are served with every meal and include bite-size, gingerbread muffins.

Guests are served by diligent waitresses in quaint, Victorian costumes. They may urge you to try the "French Silk Chocolate Creme Pie" after your meal. Do it. You'll long remember the butter and pecan crust filled with chocolate mousse and topped with whipped cream and chocolate shavings.

This is another family focus restaurant. Les and Carol Ellsworth are both always on hand to answer your questions or serve you either in the restaurant or with the gifts for sale. Carol has created many of the dishes served, and Les is an authority on English antiques. All three Ellsworth children work in the restaurant.

Be sure to visit the restroom. Both the ladies' and the men's are decorated with antiques, and the men's room contains an old clawfooted tub completely filled with growing plants.

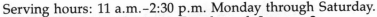

Serving hours: 11 a.m.–2:30 p.m. Monday through Saturday.
Closed: Sundays, Christmas Eve through January 2.
Lunch and afternoon snacks.
Cost of average meal: Inexpensive to moderate.
Special plates and prices: Children under 12 one-half price for half portions.
Credit cards accepted: Visa, MasterCard. Personal checks accepted.
Special occasion services: Complimentary piece of coconut cake for birthdays.
Wheelchair accommodations: Front door and restrooms.
Parking: Spacious.
No alcohol served.

The POTPOURRI House

Hickory House

(formerly the Woodbine Inn)
FM 16
Van (N.E. of Tyler)
(214) 963-7057
Owners: Lewis and Ethel
Livingston

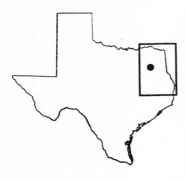

Van was originally called Who'd A' Thought It? That was before the first oil well was drilled by Pure Oil Company in Van Zandt County. Today the quiet little town is filled with Pure Oil retirees, and pump jacks still nod and bend to the ground within the city limits and in the surrounding countryside. Handsome homes and ranches evidence oil production, and inside an old Pure Oil warehouse you'll find evidence of some of the best country cooking to be found in this part of the state.

Lewis Livingston is a man who knows how to run a restaurant. He hires what he calls "good people," including mature housewives experienced in home cooking. His barbecue cook, Willie Smith, has cooked barbecue for fifty-two years. Then Lewis says he watches what comes back to the kitchen. "If they leave a lot, you know you either gave them too much or the food isn't good." As guests leave, he inquires about their satisfaction with their meal. He knows most of them by name.

The menu will vary, but typical is chicken and dumplings, purple hull peas (similar to black-eyed if you're a stranger in these parts), fried okra, and cornbread which Lewis himself makes. But it's his barbecue that Lewis likes to talk about and cater for chamber of commerce and FHA banquets. He slow-cooks it—beef, pork, ham. It is fork-tender, and you ought to try it in a sandwich or on a plate. They'll prepare it in any form to go. Ethel Livingston's homemade pies are very special, too.

Van may not look like much on the map, but you can bet that, after a meal at the Hickory House, you'll be saying, "Who'd a' thought it?"

Serving hours: 10 a.m.–8 p.m. Monday through Thursday; 10 a.m.–9
    p.m. Friday and Saturday; 11 a.m.–2 p.m. Sunday.
Closed: Labor Day, Christmas Day.
Lunch, dinner, and afternoon snacks.
Cost of average meal: Inexpensive.
No credit cards accepted. Personal checks accepted.
Wheelchair accommodations: Front door but shallow steps.
Parking: Spacious.
No alcohol served.

An old Pure Oil Company warehouse provides the setting for great country cooking in the Hickory House.

On the outside it looks as if you've gone "over the river and through the woods to Grandmother's house." Inside, the long tables with bowls of chicken and dumplings, black-eyed peas, turnip greens, watermelon pickles, and glasses of buttermilk will make you think you are at Grandma's for sure. Located alongside other old buildings in Heritage Village, the Pickett House looks just right.

You won't be surprised to learn that part of the huge, L-shaped restaurant was once a school house. The interior still has the original stove and floor. You'll sit on long benches at the big tables, and a nice young waitress will surround your place with the best country cooking you have had in a long time. In addition to the other dishes mentioned, you'll have fried chicken, speckled butter beans, sweet potatoes, hot green tomato relish, cole slaw, cornbread muffins, and peach cobbler. In cold weather there's homemade vegetable soup and chili. On Friday nights, catfish. The menu varies a bit from week to week, but no one ever left the Pickett House hungry. What's more, it's all you can eat for less than seven dollars.

Manager Nedra Roessler is a gracious, East Texas-friendly hostess who will answer any questions you have about the food, the Pickett House, or nearby Heritage Village with such enthusiasm, you'll hate to leave. To hold on to the relaxed mood of the Pickett House, stroll across to Heritage Village and be your own great-grandfather for a little while. The authentic buildings are a must for the out-of-state traveler and for young Texans.

Serving hours: 11 a.m.–3 p.m. Labor Day through March, Monday
  through Thursday; 11 a.m.–8 p.m. Friday, Saturday, and Sunday; 11
  a.m.–8 p.m. summer months, Monday through Sunday.
Closed: Christmas Day.
Lunch and dinner.
Cost of average meal: Inexpensive to moderate.
Special plates and prices: Children under six, special reduced prices.
No credit cards accepted. Personal checks accepted.
Special occasion services: Cakes.
Wheelchair accommodations: Front door.
Parking: Spacious.
No alcohol served.

Pickett House

*One mile west of town on U.S.
  Hwy. 190*
Woodville
(409) 283-8895
Owner: Don Crain
Manager: Nedra Roessler

Houston
Area
and
Gulf Coast

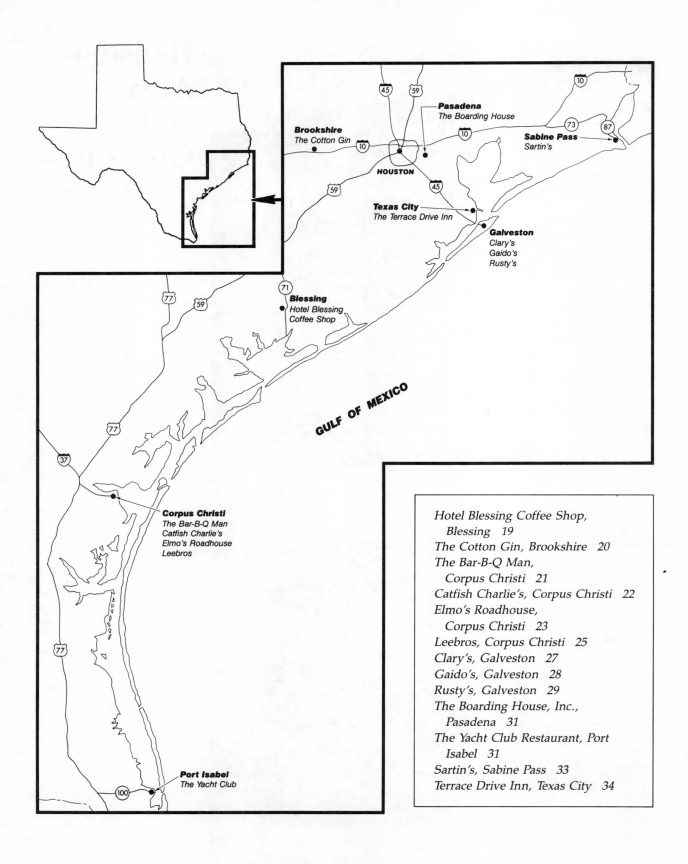

In 1902, when the post office wouldn't allow Jonathan Edward Pierce to name his town Thank God, he settled on Blessing. He built his hotel in 1906, and today either name would be appropriate for the coffee shop, which serves some of the best country cooking in the state.

If you get there early enough, say six or six-thirty, you can have breakfast and listen to the farmers and ranchers sitting at the "bull table" (as in "shoot the . . ."). Owner Helen Feldhousen says, "They've planted a lot of crops and doctored a lot of cattle at that table."

This is rice farming and ranching country, but other diners work in the oil field or at the nearby nuclear power plant. They—and you—have to decide which of the many combinations of eggs, hot cakes, and meat you are going to order. You can have one egg and one hot cake or one hot cake and meat or two eggs, two hotcakes, and meat or . . . name your combination. It's on the menu. You might prefer an egg or bacon sandwich or a ham and cheese omelet. Any of these combinations can be ordered for under three dollars at this writing. Try to match all these choices and this price anywhere in the state. Plus you can have all the coffee you can drink for twenty-five cents if you are just drinking coffee.

You'll sit family-style at the original big wood tables in the original square wood chairs. Nothing fancy. Plastic covers the tables' paper place mats. On the wall hangs an old panoramic photograph of Blessing as it looked in 1912. You can see the hotel across an empty block, even now filled with only a few small buildings.

If you arrive at lunch, the only other meal served, you can have all you can eat for four dollars. You'll get to choose from (or have them all) three meats, usually including fried chicken, sausage, and turkey; and eight vegetables, such as turnip greens, cream style and whole

Hotel Blessing Coffee Shop

10th and Avenue B
Blessing
(512) 588-6623
Owner: Helen Feldhousen

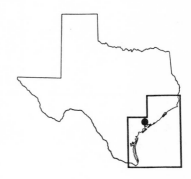

Irin 81
Hotel Blessing

kernel corn, broccoli, mashed potatoes, green beans with new potatoes, and, of course, always rice. A different dessert is made every day. If it's rice pudding, it's Saturday. Other days of the week feature peach cobbler, apple crisp, lemon and banana pudding, and sheet cake. All of this bounty is served from simmering pans on old stoves against the dining room wall, and you serve yourself. You'll wonder how working folks can return to work after the amounts you see them happily consume.

The original wall clocks at either end of the coffee shop remind the local working people when it's time to get back to the job. If you have the time, go through the double doors into the big hall of the hotel. You'll think you've stepped back in time almost eighty years. Screen doors cover the hotel room doors, iron beds sit in each room, you'll love the . . . sorry, this a book about restaurants (but don't miss peeking into the hotel!). (See *A Guide to Historic Texas Inns and Hotels*, Lone Star Books, Houston, for more details on this delightful hotel.)

Serving hours: 6 a.m.–2 p.m. Sunday through Saturday.
Closed: Christmas Day.
Breakfast and lunch.
Cost of average meal: Inexpensive.
No credit cards or personal checks accepted.
Special occasion services: Pies and cakes if given advance notice.
Wheelchair accommodations: Front door and restrooms.
Parking: Spacious.
No alcohol served.

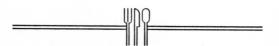

The Cotton Gin

*36 miles west of Houston on
  U.S. Hwy. 90*
Brookshire
(409) 391-4034
*Owners: Harris and Jo Ann
  Garrett, Bob Garrett, Johnny
  and Suzanne Janda*

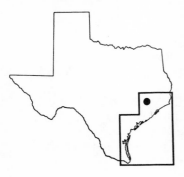

There is hardly any kind of building which can't be (and hasn't been) converted into a restaurant. You've probably eaten in a former depot or bank or inn. But there aren't many old cotton gins around that today serve as beautiful restaurants. In Brookshire, just west of Houston, there is one.

The Garretts have used the old Donigan cotton gin to create as delightful a setting for dining as you can imagine. Much of the old equipment remains with the manufacturer's name still legible on some of it. Beams have been left exposed on the high ceilings, and pleasant cedar and cypress fragrances are identifiable in the natural wood paneling. Authentic cotton-picking baskets from Mississippi hang on the walls, along with photographs of the gin in the old days. One feature often overlooked in restaurant design is lighting. Here it is soft but more than adequate for reading the menu.

In addition to a respectable wine list, the choices of entrees include almost any cut of beef anyone could desire, from prime rib to sirloin strips. Daily specials include steaks, fish, and chicken. You can also order several types of seafood. The salad bar is unusually good, espe-

cially the hominy relish, which is so delicious that regular customers keep trying to persuade the Garretts to package and sell it. Non-Southerners might want to sample the pickled watermelon rind, too, a delicacy not found in many restaurants.

Service is superb, and you get the feeling that the Garretts require the same, if not better, deportment from their fresh, young employees as they do from their guests. A no-nonsense attitude is reflected in various signs around the restaurant: "No loud talking and absolutely no profanity" (over the bar), "Proper dress required", and "Please remove hats." In this beautiful restaurant, who would want to behave any other way?

Serving hours: 6 p.m.–10 p.m. Monday through Thursday; 6 p.m.–11 p.m. Friday and Saturday. Bar open at 5 p.m.
Closed: Sundays, New Year's Day, Memorial Day, July Fourth, Labor Day, Thanksgiving, Christmas Eve, Christmas Day.
Dinner only.
Cost of average meal: Expensive.
Credit cards accepted: American Express, Visa, MasterCard, Diners Club, Carte Blanche. Personal checks accepted upon approval.
Special occasion services: Cake.
Special required dress: No hats worn.
Reservations requested.
Wheelchair accommodations: Front door and restrooms.
Parking: Spacious.

Remember, you can often notice certain indicators of a restaurant's quality before you eat there—things like the mixture of police cars, pickups, and expensive cars sitting outside. *Blue Highways* author William Least Heat Moon looks for wall calendars from local businesses, suggesting that their owners are frequent guests. Another good sign of a restaurant's excellence is an array of certificates and plaques near the cash register indicating the owner's activity in the Texas Restaurant Association. At the Bar-B-Q Man, you will see numerous TRA awards which the De Shields family has earned with

The Bar-B-Q Man

Off I-37 S., one block south of
La Quinta
Corpus Christi
(512) 888-4248
Owners: Malcolm O.
De Shields and Malcolm T.
De Shields

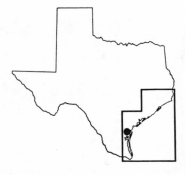

their good food, good service, and attention to their guests' satisfaction.

Once you taste the salubrious brisket or ribs, you'll appreciate the big stacks of mesquite outside. You can combine up to four of the tender, mesquite-smoked meats on the combination plate, adding ham and sausage. You also get beans, cole slaw or potato salad, a big onion slice, and a great dill pickle slice. If you aren't acquainted with the personality of a jalapeño pepper, approach the halved one on your plate with caution. Add a little of the Bar-B-Q Man's original, piquant barbecue sauce to your beans, and ladle it over your meat. The homemade rolls are light as a whisper.

In addition to serving diners in their three dining rooms and in a separate bar, the De Shields can serve up to a thousand on their covered pavilion and adjoining dining room behind the restaurant. Here they often cater wedding receptions, anniversaries, and other large parties.

Barbecue by the pound and all the side orders of beans, potato salad, cole slaw, and barbecue sauce are available to go. You can even order ahead a whole smoked ham or boneless, whole, turkey breast.

Corpus Christi has an unusually large number of good, home-owned restaurants, but if you ask almost anyone in town where the best barbecue is, you'll be told "The Bar-B-Q Man."

Serving hours: 11 a.m.–10 p.m. Monday through Friday.
Closed: Saturdays, Sundays, New Year's Day, January 2, Memorial Day, first week in June, Labor Day, Thanksgiving, Christmas Day through January 2.
Lunch and dinner.
Cost of average meal: Moderate.
Special plates: All meats available a la carte. Children's plates.
Credit cards accepted: American Express, Visa, MasterCard, Diners Club, Carte Blanche. Personal checks accepted.
Special occasion services: Private rooms available if arranged in advance.
Wheelchair accommodations: Front door.
Parking: Spacious.

Catfish Charlie's

McArdle at Airline in Crossroads Center
Corpus Christi
(512) 993-0362
Owner: R. B. Langham
Manager: Vicki Galloway

Many of today's young restaurateurs worked as waiters or busboys while attending college. As they were serving or clearing off tables, they said to themselves, "I'll bet I could make a living in this line of work. First, I'd make sure I served good, strong iced tea. Then I'd buy only good napkins. Then. . ." Thus were a number of the newer home-owned restaurants in the state begun. R. B. Langham, owner of Catfish Charlie's, started this way, and recently he opened another restaurant with the same name in San Antonio on Wurzbach at Interstate 10.

Catfish Charlie's is the kind of casual, Texany place of which people impulsively say, "Hey, let's go over to Catfish Charlie's and eat catfish

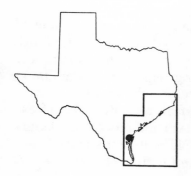

and shrimp." Sitting in the high-ceilinged dining room, you can tell who the regular diners are by the easy way they saunter in and go directly to a favorite table. Before you can make up your mind what to order, a cute, young, overalled waitress brings you a basket of hot hush puppies laced with jalapeños. Then you have to make the big decision: a big bowl of thick, spicy, seafood gumbo or a dozen fried oysters or maybe both. Seafood is plentiful in Corpus Christi, of course, but here you can have it, as well as several side dishes, with a cajun touch: bayou-style fried shrimp; cajun, country-style, fried frog legs; or Bayou Teche creole shrimp on rice. The menu "guarontees" you will like their smoke-flavored, creole-style red beans. They're one of the restaurant's tastiest dishes. Restaurant critics seldom mention the merits or shortcomings of that Southern staple, cole slaw. Catfish Charlie's is one of the few restaurants serving *sincere slaw*, crunchy and sweet, the cabbage and other ingredients sliced to respectable thickness. Good for them!

Vicki Galloway, the charming manager of the restaurant, is a graduate of Corpus Christi's Del Mar College, with a degree in restaurant management. Her training, plus Langham's personal interest in his restaurant and his guests, make a combination you will recognize in the great service and friendly atmosphere.

You can order domestic longnecks or Mexico's Tecate, along with other imported beers and wines.

Serving hours: 11 a.m. until closing (9 p.m.-ish) daily.
Closed: New Year's Day, Super Bowl Day, Thanksgiving, Christmas Day.
Lunch and dinner.
Cost of average meal: Moderate.
Special plates: Child's plate on any entree (catfish, shrimp, fried chicken, chicken fried steak).
Credit cards accepted: Visa, MasterCard. Personal checks accepted.
Special occasion services: Complimentary ice cream and crew sings "Happy Birthday."
Wheelchair accommodations: Front door with ramp.
Parking: Spacious.

Elmo's Roadhouse

I-37 at Violet, 15 miles from
downtown
Corpus Christi
(512) 241-0621
Owner: Elmo V. Jackson
Manager: Chris Dionne

If you're old enough to remember when service stations were called *filling stations*, you'll appreciate Elmo's Roadhouse probably more than anyone. Elmo Jackson has lined the interior walls of his barn-size restaurant with age-tinged advertising signs for oil companies, soft drinks, cigars, and cigarettes: Mobil Oil's Pegasus, Sinclair's dinosaur, Magnolia's blossom, Triple X root beer, Grapette, five-cent Coca Cola. Old gas pumps advertise gas for thirteen cents a gallon. Vintage photos show us what service stations used to look like back when attendants automatically wiped your windshield and checked your tires.

A sign in the lobby tells you right off what to expect: "There are hundreds of restaurants in Corpus Christi, yet today you selected Elmo's. You're entitled to good food and service every time you visit our restaurant. If, for some reason you don't feel you have received both, please let the management know. We want your business and sincerely appreciate it. Elmo Jackson." The sign sets the tone for everything in the restaurant, and it all lives up to premium expectations.

If you're new to the Corpus Christi area, you'll wonder where all the diners come from as they fill the split-level dining rooms for lunch and dinner. After your meal, you'll understand why they don't mind driving the distance from town or outlying regions to enjoy Elmo's food. For lunch, his "Running Board Specials" change every day. A fresh flounder with Mornay sauce is one feature, with always-fresh vegetables from a choice of four. Fresh squash and broccoli in December is a rare treat in any restaurant. "Rumble Seat Sandwiches," such as a Super Club with a chicken filet, topped with melted cheese, bacon and "all the fixin's," are served with crispy potato shells. "To Settle the Road Dust" beverages include imported and domestic beers by the pitcher, glass, or in longnecks, as well as house wines and soft drinks. A full bar is located on one level of the restaurant.

The evening menu and also Sunday lunch offer "Filler Up Family Style Dinners." Entree choices for one, two, or four people include

Both inside and outside, Elmo's Roadhouse is a nostalgic place to dine for those who remember thirteen-cent gasoline and rumble seats.

sirloin steak, fresh water catfish, fried shrimp, fajitas, frog legs, and fried flounder. All dinners come with a bucket of salad, a bowl of beans or fries, and hot bread from the restaurant's bake shop.

Special children's plates include chicken fried steak, fried shrimp, catfish, or a fried chicken leg. All the desserts are made at the restaurant.

Elmo Jackson grew up in a Corpus Christi restaurant family, and his exposure to the business shows in every detail of his Roadhouse. Female guests appreciate the antique plate in the glass case in the lobby. Its inscription reads:

"Wives that work and do the dishes
Should be granted these three wishes:
A grateful mate, a well-kissed cheek,
A restaurant dinner every week."

Serving hours: 11:30 a.m.–2 p.m. Tuesday through Friday; 11 a.m.–2:30 p.m. Sunday; 5 p.m.–10 p.m. Tuesday through Sunday; 5 p.m.–10:30 p.m. Friday and Saturday.
Closed: Mondays, Christmas Eve, Christmas Day.
Lunch, dinner, and afternoon snacks in the bar.
Cost of average meal: Moderate.
Special plates: Children's plates.
Credit cards accepted: American Express, Visa, MasterCard. No personal checks accepted.
Special occasion services: Cakes for birthdays and anniversaries.
Wheelchair accommodations: Front door.
Special required dress: "Casual but not trashy."
Reservations: Requested for groups of eight or more.
Parking: Limited.

When a restaurant owner tells you that another restaurant is his "most favorite restaurant in the whole city," you'd better listen. This is the kind of accolade Bob Lee has earned from a fellow restaurateur. Bob manages Leebros, while his brother Larry owns and operates Chung Mei, the Chinese restaurant in Corpus Christi once owned by their late father, DuLit Lee.

Leebros announces on its sign and its menu that it serves "seafood and delectables." It also offers impeccable service, soft lighting, quiet

Leebros

5817 Weber in Weber Square
Corpus Christi
(512) 853-9881
Owners: Bob and Cindy Lee,
Larry Lee

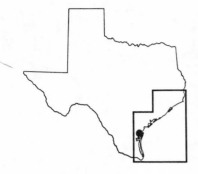

surroundings, interesting decor, and the gracious hospitality of Bob and Cindy Lee. Take time to look at the prints and original paintings. Some are very amusing. Cindy did all the stained glass.

The seafood entrees are prepared in innovative as well as traditional styles. A more limited lunch menu includes the "Cousteau," a delicate crepe folded around shrimp, scallops, and mushrooms, sauteed in sherry and topped with Mornay sauce. Your salad will be covered with a novel, crunchy nest of fried egg roll strips. For dinner, scallops devotees will want to order "Leebros Scallops," lightly coated with flour and braised in a soya-sauterne sauce. Fresh snow pea pods are also paired with scallops along with mushrooms and onions in a rich seafood sauce.

Leebros uses Alaskan Snow Crab, perhaps the best in the world. Ixtapa shrimp are sauteed and blended with garlic, onions, soy sauce, sherry, and sour cream. In fact, almost any seafood you can name, along with frog legs, steak, and chicken are all on the menu.

It's easy to see why Leebros is the regular meeting place for a number of Corpus Christi organizations including the Lions Club, Sertoma Club, and Home Builders. A restaurant can receive no better endorsement than being the chosen eating place for such groups.

Serving hours: 11:30 a.m.–2 p.m. Monday through Friday; 5 p.m.–10 p.m. Monday through Thursday; 5 p.m.–11 p.m. Friday and Saturday.
Closed: Sundays, seldom closed on major holidays.
Lunch and dinner.
Cost of average meal: Lunch—inexpensive to moderate; dinner—moderate to expensive.
Special plates: For children, fried fish, chopped sirloin, and fried shrimp.
For dieters, owner will prepare food for special needs.
Credit cards accepted: American Express, Visa, Diners Club, Carte Blanche.
Local checks accepted with identification.
Special occasion services: Complimentary cake with candle for birthdays. For anniversaries a glass or bottle of champagne, "depending on duration of marriage."
Wheelchair accommodations: Front door and restrooms.
Reservations: Required for parties of five or more.
Parking: Spacious.

Leebros is a beautiful, expertly run Corpus Christi restaurant which local service clubs choose for their regular meeting place.

You'll drive across the island almost as far as you can go to the east end, but it's worth the easy drive. Clary's is located on Offatt Bayou, and if you take a window table for dinner, you can watch the sun set on the boat channel leading from the bayou and see the lights wink on across the water. The restaurant is one of the most relaxing on the island and also one of the most interesting.

Owner Clary Milburn brings an energy and pride to his restaurant which shows in every dish. The first thing you see on the menu is his promise "If we don't think it's special, we will not serve it." He lives up to his promise with his Louisiana style, hot, boiled shrimp appetizer. (That's hot as in seasonings, folks.) You peel them yourself, but if that doesn't bother you, you'll agree they definitely are special. His seafood gumbo is a thick, spicy soup with whole shrimp tucked into the rice and other good things.

Talk to one of the Milburn sons who works in the restaurant—Wayne, Dwayne, or Dexter—and you'll hear the same pride and enthusiasm for anything on the menu but especially for the flame-broiled shrimp and plump charcoal-broiled shrimp in a butter sauce.

At Clary's you are sure to find dishes not served anywhere else. Clary likes to talk about his culinary creations such as "Oysters 32." Supposedly, there are only twenty-nine ways to prepare oysters. Or were, until Clary invented a few new twists. Oyster lovers are sure to add them to their list of favorites. Clary also urges guests to order his "Off the Menu" specialties. One of them could be a dish he has just created or a new version of an old recipe. He once spent an entire night in the kitchen, working on exactly the right thickness for his gumbo. At 4 a.m., he got it right, sat down to think about his success, fell asleep, awoke at 7:30, and went back to work for the day in the restaurant.

Because he worked in a restaurant kitchen and as a waiter when he was younger, Clary appreciates diners' attitudes toward chefs. "They're the least appreciated restaurant employee," he says. Thus he created a special room, separated from another dining room with a sound-absorbent glass and carpet on the floor and walls. Diners who like the idea of the chef himself coming out and explaining the preparations of certain dishes can sit in this room, and give "our compliments to the chef" in person.

Clary's

I-45 at Teichmann Rd. Exit
Galveston
(409) 740-0771
Owner: Clary Milburn

Serving hours: 11 a.m.–2:30 p.m., 6 p.m.–10 p.m. Monday through
    Saturday.
Closed: Sundays, New Year's Day, July Fourth, Thanksgiving and
    several days following, Christmas Eve, Christmas Day.
Lunch and dinner.
Cost of average meal: Expensive.
Credit cards accepted: American Express, Visa, MasterCard. Personal
    checks accepted only from known customers.
Special occasion services: Cakes for birthdays and anniversaries.
Wheelchair accommodations: Front door and restrooms.
Reservations suggested.
Parking: Spacious with parking valet on duty.

Gaido's

39th (Mike Gaido Blvd.) and Seawall Blvd.
Galveston
(409) 762-0115
Owners: The Mike Gaido family: Mickey, Paul, and Wayne

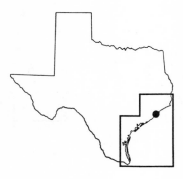

Ask most Texas inlanders what comes to mind when they think of Galveston, and the answer will frequently be "Gaido's." Since 1911, when the first Gaido's (pronounced *guy-doz*) was located atop Murdoch's Bathhouse on the Gulf side of Seawall Boulevard, the restaurant has been synonymous with Galveston. Its significance was proved again recently when the city named Thirty-ninth Street Mike Gaido Boulevard.

While Galveston has many fine restaurants with great seafood, Gaido's is the Olympus of seafood lovers. Poseidon himself didn't eat fresher fish. If you don't believe it's fresh, ask if they will let you visit their kitchen. The proof is everywhere, along with signs reminding waiters of the high standards of service the Gaido brothers demand.

To meet these standards, waiters must pass two written and two oral tests and must be apprenticed for two weeks. The result is waiters who not only know how to serve a table of guests but who are informed about every dish on the menu.

It could easily take you half an hour just to study the beverage list. Gaido's lists over one hundred domestic and imported beers. The wine list is equally impressive. To help you decide, each appetizer and entree has several suggested wines listed by number. Or ask your waiter for a suggestion or for information. He or she will positively know the answer. In "honor" of the 1983 hurricane, Alicia, one drink is named "Alicia for Two" with six different kinds of rum. Nonalcoholic "mocktails" include a marguerita, strawberry daiquiri, pina colada, and "Typhoon for Two."

"Angels on Horseback" can be ordered by the half dozen or dozen for an appetizer or light meal. They are oysters, wrapped in ham, skewered with fresh pineapple and charcoal-broiled. Heavenly!

Any edible sea creature that swims anywhere near Galveston is on the menu, each one prepared in several delectable ways. You'll agree that the red snapper do not die in vain. The vegetables are fresh, and the buttered sesame rolls with apple jelly are scrumptious. An almost-forgotten amenity comes at the end of your meal in finger bowls with floating lemon slices.

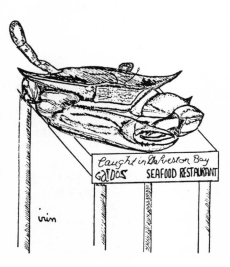

You'll want to look at the nautical antiques collection in the dining room, and crystal-fanciers will appreciate the large, lead crystal collection in the lobby. A well-stocked gift shop off the lobby carries unusual and high-quality Galveston souvenirs (such as this book).

Serving hours: 11:30 a.m.–10 p.m. every day except Monday.
Closed: Mondays, September through April, New Year's Day,
    Thanksgiving, Christmas Eve, Christmas Day.
Lunch and dinner.
Cost of average meal: Moderate to expensive.
Special plates: Children's and senior citizens' plates.
Credit cards accepted: American Express, Visa, MasterCard. Personal
    checks accepted.
Special occasion services: Cakes.
Wheelchair accommodations: Front door and restrooms.
Parking: Spacious.

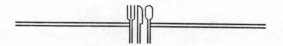

Rusty's

*8th St. (Postoffice) and Avenue
    E (St. Mary's)
Galveston
(409) 763-1394
Owners: Russ and Pat Eitel*

Any restaurant in Galveston is easy to find if a visitor knows that almost every numbered or lettered street has another name—a handy bit of information to have and one which most townsfolk forget to tell you when giving directions. Rusty's is located on the edge of the downtown area. It also helps to know that Eighth Street (Postoffice) is one way going east, so if you're approaching from Seawall Boulevard, you might want to come up Ninth Street and turn right on Avenue E (St. Mary's).

Russ and Pat Eitel have covered their walls with nostalgia: an entire wall shelved with old books, photos of somebody's ancestors, a collection of photographs showing Forest Hills Country Club tennis champions of several decades past, and other photos of Galveston's native son whose directional mistake brought him fame ("Wrong Way Corrigan", you may remember, thought he was flying to California but wound up in Ireland). Latticed windows and hanging lamps suggestive of old gas lights cast a soft glow over the tables.

All this atmosphere is not the only reason for going to Rusty's. Lunch guests who are regular diners enjoy homemade soups, a good salad bar contained in an old Coca Cola case, and sumptuous sandwiches such as the "Mushacado," a meal in itself with fresh, sliced mushrooms, avocado, and melted cheese on fresh, homemade, wheat bread. The "Elissa" sandwich is named for the 1877 squarerigger docked in West Bay. It layers tuna, avocado, lettuce, and tomato between slices of whole wheat bread. The bread is for sale by the loaf—two pounds of stone-ground wheat, honey, yeast, and butter. All sandwiches come with your choice of potato chips or potato salad. Take the potato salad. It's chunky and oniony and far above average restaurant potato salad.

Lots of atmosphere and sumptuous sandwiches are two reasons for Rusty's popularity.

The dinner menu adds steaks, including chicken fried, and also shrimp and seafood. "Chicken Ashton Villa," named after one of Galveston's most beautiful historic homes, is chicken stuffed with ham, melted Swiss cheese, and German spices, served over a wild rice blend.

Libations include hot or cold spiced tea, which is full of cloves and other spices. Among the more potent drinks is the "Wrong Way Corrigan," a combination of island juices and dark rum.

Live entertainment on Friday and Saturday evenings features music in a mixture of folk, country, blues, and easy listening. During summer months, you are apt to find musical performers also during the week.

Serving hours: 11 a.m.–11 p.m. Monday through Thursday; 11 a.m.–12 p.m. Friday and Saturday.
Closed: Sundays, New Year's Day, Thanksgiving, Christmas Day through New Year's Day.
Lunch and dinner.
Cost of average meal: Inexpensive to moderate.
Credit cards accepted: American Express, Visa, MasterCard. Personal checks accepted.
Special occasion services: Cake with sparkler and song.
Wheelchair accommodations: Front door and restrooms.
Parking: Limited.

At The Boarding House in Pasadena, it's no frills and no nonsense. Signs on the wall read: "We really don't care how you did it up north," and "If you are not served in 30 seconds, we shoot one waitress and one cook," and "Please take all you want but eat all you take." But the owners are friendly and the food the best, however simple. Perhaps the simplicity of the place is the main part of its success.

Leon and Verna Phillips serve meals to celebrities en route to Texas' biggest honky-tonk, Gilley's, and to ordinary folk like the clean-cut young men who rent their rooms in surrounding houses and eat at The Boarding House. These regular diners know the Phillipses mean what they say on the sign which reads "The menu today is whatever's on the table. No substitutes."

"Whatever's on the table" includes fried chicken, meat loaf, ten vegetables such as butter beans, turnip greens, corn, green beans, and big hot rolls. No desserts unless you're a boarder. If you're lucky, you'll arrive on a day they're serving chicken and dumplings. It's real Southern cooking—"just good home cooking", the Phillipses call it.

The restaurant was formerly called Leasure's before the Phillipses took it over fewer than ten years ago. Apparently many Pasadenans don't know where it is, but Verna Phillips says, "Get on your CB and any trucker can tell you." After one meal there, you'll never have trouble finding your way back.

Make a note: The Boarding House is open Thanksgiving Day.

Serving hours: 5:30 a.m.–9 a.m., 11 a.m.–7 p.m. Monday through Friday.
Closed: Saturday and Sunday to the public, New Year's Day, Memorial Day, July Fourth, Labor Day, Christmas Day.
Breakfast, lunch, and dinner.
Cost of average meal: Inexpensive.
No credit cards accepted. Cash only.
Wheelchair accommodations: Front door and restrooms.
Reservations: Only for an unusually large party.
Parking: Spacious.
No alcohol served.

The Boarding House, Inc.

219 S. Randall, take Pasadena Exit off I-45 to Randall, turn right, second block
Pasadena
(713) 472-9102
Owners: E. Leon and Verna Phillips

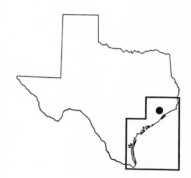

Telling some friends that you're going to Port Isabel to eat at The Yacht Club is a little like telling them you've just been given a trip around the world or a new car or free groceries for a year. Don't expect shared joy and anticipation. They may not even be polite. Especially if they themselves have enjoyed one of the seafood meals The Yacht Club is famous for. What you'll get is undisguised envy.

During the 1920s, visitors to Port Isabel considered only one destination for the best in seafood and hotel accommodations. Originally built as a private club for prominent Rio Grande Valley families, the

The Yacht Club Restaurant

700 Yturria
Port Isabel
(512) 943-1301
Owners: Ron and Lynn Speier
Manager: Bob Speier

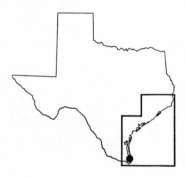

hotel and restaurant served the public from 1929 until 1969. In recent years it has been restored to its original, luxurious resort atmosphere and now offers the same consistently fine seafood plus newly-decorated room accommodations.

Located on the North Shore of Port Isabel, its Spanish-style tower can be seen from Highway 100 which leads to South Padre Island. The original white stucco still covers the outside, and the moment you step inside you'll feel you have stepped back in time. The owners retained all the beautiful Spanish influence in the white walls and dark-beamed ceilings, with deep red carpets and draperies for contrast.

In the dining rooms you'll be surrounded with photographs of visitors from the Yacht Club's early years, some in the now quaint-looking bathing suits. Naturally, there are also pictures of proud fishermen showing off their catches. Huge, mounted specimens of marlin, barracuda, and tuna hang on the walls as testimony to one of the favorite sports along the Texas coast.

Above the tables, slowly revolving fans and amber-shaded lamps add to the nostalgia. Pewter dinnerware and instantaneous service which never falters contribute further to your feeling of being the pampered guest, an impression you will not soon forget.

The menu, of course, consists almost entirely of fish selections with a few seafood and steak combinations. Don't even *think* that this will be the only time you'll ever eat here or you'll go crazy trying to decide on what to order. The shrimp probably swam close by in the Gulf of Mexico the night before and were caught by some of the 800 or so shrimp boats which fish the area. Your lobster may have just arrived from Maine. The broiled red snapper filet is a house specialty which the owners affirm was caught seventeen to thirty miles offshore. That's fresh!

A big platter containing a sampling of almost every type of fish served includes shrimp, scallops, oysters, stuffed crab, and a fish filet. If you're the only one in the party who doesn't particularly care for seafood, try the fried scallops. You may become an immediate convert.

Two seatings are offered for dinner, and the earlier one is usually less crowded and allows time for strolling through the different dining rooms and appreciating the beauty of this memorable place.

The extensive bar menu encourages you to sip something "Before," "During", and "After" with separate lists of suggestions. "Before" you might have a fresh banana daiquiri or a Yacht Club Special, "a light blend of rum and things." "During" you can have almost any wine you can think of, and "after", you can end with Irish coffee, a brandy freeze with ice cream, or Cappucino.

Serving hours: 5 p.m.–10 p.m. every day except Wednesday.
Closed: Wednesdays, Thanksgiving, Christmas Day.
Dinner only.
Cost of average meal: Expensive.
Credit cards accepted: American Express, Visa, MasterCard, Diners
    Club, Carte Blanche. Only local, personal checks which have been
    approved before eating are accepted.
Special occasion services: Birthday cake with a sparkler and "Happy
    Birthday" sung.
Wheelchair accommodations: Front door and restrooms.
Reservations requested.
Parking: Spacious.

Things which are hard to obtain are often costly: truffles, true love, and canned crab meat. If you've ever wondered about the crab meat, spend a half hour or so at Sartin's, cracking crab claws. Swarms of diners swear by them, but if you're squeamish about your fish being served looking much the way it did before it was caught, stay away from the barbecued crab. Instead, order the spicy stuffed crab or fried shrimp.

The setting and atmosphere are as casual as you will find in a Gulf Coast restaurant. They don't claim that cracking crab claws or eating the charcoal-covered, barbecued crabs is neat. Rolls of paper towels are provided for lots of hand-wiping. The rustic interior and lighted beer signs on the walls seem just right. Friendly waitresses wear T-shirts which read, "We got the crabs."

You can be sure your fish is fresh. The Sartins have their own fishing boat and go out every day to find your shrimp, red snapper, flounder, crabs, and oysters. Returning guests come back in their private planes from Dallas, Fort Worth, Houston, Lufkin, and Lake

Sartin's

*13 miles south of Port Arthur
Sabine Pass
(409) 971-2158
Owners: Charles and Jerri
    Sartin*

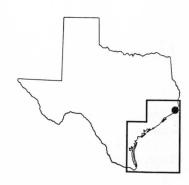

Only a short drive from Port Arthur, Sartin's serves some of the freshest seafood on the Gulf Coast.

Charles for Sartin's seafood. The menu promises "Ours woke up in the Gulf this morning." Can't get much fresher than that.

Serving hours: 11 a.m.–10 p.m. Monday through Sunday.
Closed: Christmas Day.
Lunch, dinner, and afternoon snacks.
Cost of average meal: Inexpensive to expensive.
Special plates: Children's and senior citizens' plates.
No credit cards accepted. Personal checks accepted.
Special occasion services: Birthday crab with candle, song.
Wheelchair accommodations: Front door and restrooms.
Reservations requested or required: Six or more on weekends.
Parking: Spacious.

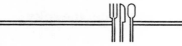

Terrace Drive Inn

814 Ninth Avenue N.
Texas City
(409) 948-2519
Owner: Rose Hinson

You probably thought there were no places left which still serve Frito pie or a chili-and-cheese-covered weiner in a bun and call it a Coney Island. How about a place that serves homemade chili every day? And has car hop service, too! Well, there's the Terrace Drive Inn in Texas City, and it does all of those things and a lot more.

People don't come to the Terrace for decor or atmosphere. They come for the shrimp gumbo on Friday and homemade vegetable soup, spaghetti, and meat balls, and hamburgers. A different special

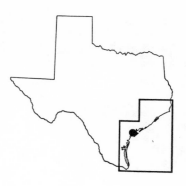

every day may include corned beef and cabbage or chicken fried steak, maybe apple cobbler. Head cook Rita Rivers has been at the Terrace for thirty-two years. That should be proof of how good the food is.

Many returning diners ate here when they were just kids. The police used to have to direct traffic into the parking lot, the crowds were so big. The awning was still up over the parking lot when the Terrace was featured on "The Eyes of Texas" TV show. That was before hurrican Alicia swept over the Texas coast in 1983 and blew it off. But the restaurant's car hops continue to bring customers their food on the old metal trays the same way customers have been served here for over thirty years.

Rose Hinson is a nice, no-nonsense lady who started the restaurant in the fifties. Her knowledge of running a restaurant shows in this simple but outstanding example of good, home cooking in an expertly-operated, home-owned restaurant.

Serving hours: 7 a.m.–10 to 11 p.m. Mondays through Saturdays.
Closed: Sundays, Thanksgiving and Christmas Day.
Breakfast, lunch, dinner, and afternoon snacks.
Cost of average meal: Inexpensive.
Special plates: Small lunch specials for anyone.
No credit cards accepted. Personal checks accepted.
No wheelchair accommodations.
Parking: Spacious.
Beer only.

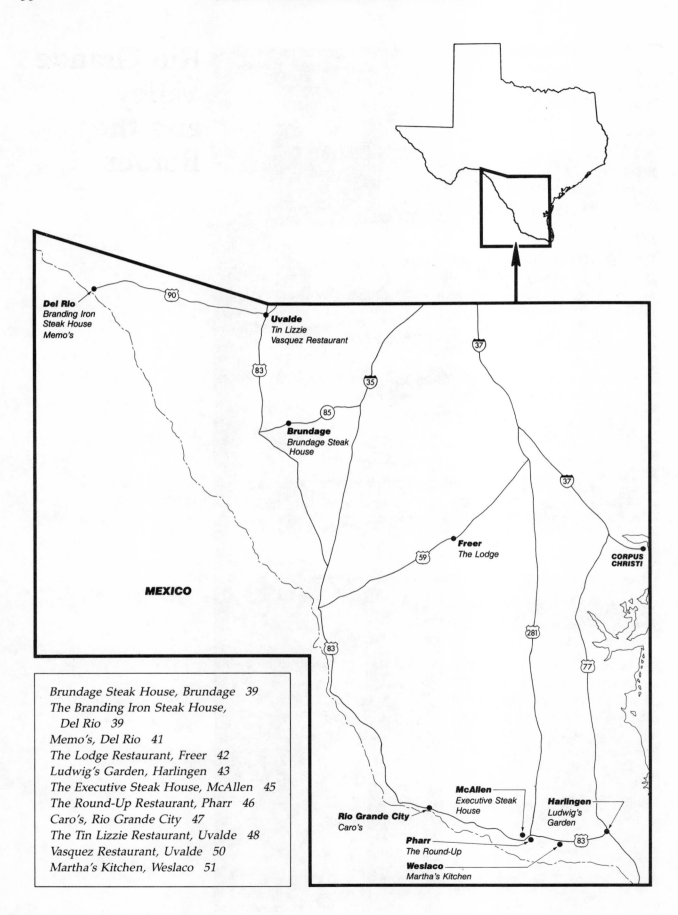

Del Rio
*Branding Iron
Steak House
Memo's*

Uvalde
*Tin Lizzie
Vasquez Restaurant*

Brundage
*Brundage Steak
House*

Freer
The Lodge

MEXICO

**CORPUS
CHRISTI**

McAllen
*Executive Steak
House*

Harlingen
*Ludwig's
Garden*

Rio Grande City
Caro's

Pharr
The Round-Up

Weslaco
Martha's Kitchen

From 1929 until 1943, the building in which this restaurant is located today served as the Brundage School. The only regrettable thing is that the earlier owners removed almost every evidence of its original use, and no suggestion of it is now visible. Imaginative diners look around for Big Chief tablets, a blackboard, maybe an old teacher's desk. Apparently, such oversights don't matter to the scores of people who drive out to this little off-the-beaten-path restaurant on the dirt road off of the highway.

Even if you aren't a chicken fried steak lover, don't pass this restaurant by. They are rightly proud of both their CFS and onion rings and say they sell more of those two items than anything else. The portion is generous, the price modest, and instead of the cream gravy underneath the steak or on top, here it is served in a little bowl on your platter. They also offer other steak cuts: T-bones, sirloin strips, pepper steak, steak a la Tampiqueña, etc. In addition, they feature "fresh-dressed quail," an entree you'll find frequently in this part of the state because of the abundance of quail. The menu also lists seafood, Mexican plates, and both hot and cold sandwiches.

Homemade biscuits are hot and airy and seem an appropriate accompaniment to a meal in a country restaurant. On weekends you can end your lunch or dinner with homemade pie—chocolate, coconut, or lemon.

Serving hours: 11 a.m.–9:30 p.m. Tuesday through Saturday.
Closed: Sunday, Monday, New Year's Day, July Fourth, Thanksgiving, Christmas Eve, Christmas Day.
Lunch and dinner.
Cost of average meal: Inexpensive.
Credit cards accepted: Visa, MasterCard. Personal checks accepted.
Wheelchair accommodations: Front door and restrooms.
Parking: Spacious.

Brundage Steak House

13 miles east of Carrizo Springs, off State Hwy. 85
Brundage
(512) 457-2627
Owners: C. W. Fisher and Sabrina Stansberry

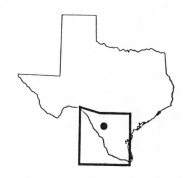

The Branding Iron Steak House is such a fun place it could have brightened even the surly moods of the infamous Judge Roy Bean who is buried in Del Rio. The dining rooms are crammed with countless western memorabilia; authentic branding irons, a horse hair bridle, a pair of ladies' shoes from the 1800s, ranching tools, and other reminders of the days when this Border town was the stopping-off place for Forty-niners and other western pioneers.

The rustic decor, including brick floors, is a perfect setting for an entertaining evening. "This is not the place to come for a quiet dinner," owner Thelma Aubry laughs. Soon after you're seated, you understand what she means.

At the steel guitar, entertainer Richie Dell plays and sings all the old tear-jerkers such as "Blue Christmas" and "Help Me Make It Through the Night," but when he switches to something lighter, say "The Rose of San Antone," he is accompanied by Julio, the cook, who

The Branding Iron Steak House

3802 U.S. Hwy. 90 W.
Del Rio
(512) 775-7853
Owner: Thelma Aubry

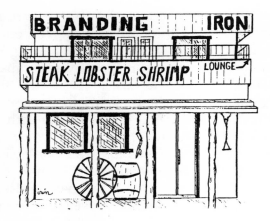

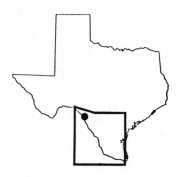

bangs out accompanying rhythm with kitchen tools on his stove and applauds the close of each song with the clang of a cowbell or the toot of an old auto horn. Occasionally Julio grabs his dancing partner behind the counter and gives her a whirl around the grill. Fortunately, she is a life-size doll, so a slight brush against the stove won't hurt too much.

You may wonder when Julio has time to prepare your steak, he is so busy being a part of the act, but he does, and you won't be disappointed in any of the mesquite-broiled steaks on the menu. The "Super Kicker Top Sirloin" is fourteen ounces, and the "Cowgirl," a New York strip, is twelve ounces. You can also choose from sirloin chunks on a skewer, a "Wrangler Burger," jumbo shrimp or lobster. The baked potatoes are Texas-big. If you're new to that favorite side dish and seasoning in ninety percent of Tex-Mex food, nibble with care the small bowl of jalapeños they'll bring you. Those innocent-looking little green peppers are pickled fire to most palates.

Upstairs, Mac runs the lounge, and on Thursday through Saturday nights you can enjoy live entertainment there. You'll sit at tables made from antique wagon wheels covered with glass. A wide TV screen is usually on during week nights, showing sports events or special movies. Mac is a bartending school graduate, so you can be sure of a good drink.

The lighting downstairs is soft, the food is good, and the atmosphere is fun. *But not rowdy.* Ms. Aubry doesn't allow any bad language nor rough behavior, so best you remember. She's tiny, but she's the boss.

Serving hours: 5 p.m.–11 p.m. Monday through Thursday; 5 p.m.–12
  p.m. Friday and Saturday.
Closed: Sundays, New Year's Day, Thanksgiving, Christmas Day.
Dinner only.
Cost of average meal: Expensive.
Credit cards accepted: Visa, MasterCard. Local checks accepted.
Special occasion services: For birthday or anniversary a "cake" (a
  hamburger bun covered with whipped cream, some cherries, and a
  candle).
Wheelchair accommodations: Side door, restrooms.
Parking: Spacious.

It probably isn't one bit true that Texans talk more about the weather than people who live in other states. But in Texas the unexpected suddenness of flash floods and other unwelcomed natural events do provide plenty of conversational subject matter. At Memo's Restaurant, the best view of San Felipe Creek is through a long row of picture windows. There diners can watch the ordinarily clear green waters slide quietly by through thick, grassy banks that slope steeply downward from the restaurant. But after an October downpour dumped three inches of rain from Border skies onto Del Rio, San Felipe Creek was a muddy torrent that brought back fearful memories to owner "Blondie" Calderon. He remembered back in the fifties when rain pushed San Felipe's waters all the way up to his restaurant doors.

Weather is far from the most interesting subject to discuss with Blondie. He likes to talk about the nearly forty years his family has operated Memo's. In the kitchen, he'll assure you, his mother is still "the head honcho." He is understandably proud of all the dishes she helps prepare for his menu, described accurately as "Superbly Mexican." Some of the selections which you probably won't find on menus in many other Mexican restaurants include a guizado plate, a "kind of steak," Blondie explains. He'll give you more details, but you won't really care how it is prepared, it is so good. Then there are Portuguese tortillas, pericos ("loaded nachos"), and of course, great enchiladas, tacos, chalupas, and all the rest. If you can't decide what to order, let Blondie choose for you. You won't be disappointed. Steaks, burgers, and sandwiches are also available.

The bar serves an interesting list of mixed drinks, including one called "El Pancho Villa," which is a straight shot of tequila. *That* should rouse the revolutionary in you.

Of course it's important that Blondie runs a great restaurant with superior food, but if you know anything at all about musical performers, specifically Ray Price, you know that perhaps Blondie's best-known claim to fame is the fact that he is Price's accompanist on the piano, the vibes, and drums. He has also produced an album of his own entitled *Feelings*. Tuesday nights at Memo's are jam session nights, featuring Blondie, three of his brothers, and some musician friends. You'll need a reservation because almost everyone in Del Rio tries to come. Blondie has been with Price for almost twenty years, so you may have seen him on the network talk shows or perhaps live in concert. For the benefit of an admiring visiting writer, even though it wasn't a Tuesday night jam session, Blondie went over to his baby grand and played "For the Good Times," one of Price's best.

The restaurant walls are filled with photographs of his entertainer friends: Doc Severinsen, Charlie Pride, Kris Kristofferson, Johnny Rodriguez, and many others. Among the photos is one which explains Calderon's nickname—it is hard to believe even with the proof staring out at you—a photo of a beautiful two-year-old child, as blonde as any youngster you've ever seen.

Memo's

804 Losoya Street
Del Rio
(512) 775-8104
Owners: Mr. and Mrs. Moisés
*   Calderon*

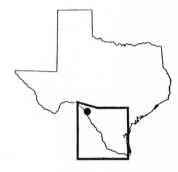

Serving hours: 11 a.m.–2 p.m., 6 p.m.–10 p.m. Monday through
   Saturday; 6 p.m.–10 p.m. Sundays.
Closed: New Year's Day, Labor Day, Thanksgiving, Christmas Day.
Lunch and dinner.
Cost of average meal: Inexpensive.
No credit cards accepted. Personal checks accepted.
Special occasion services: Wedding receptions and private parties.
Wheelchair accommodations: Front door.
Special required dress: No bathing suits.
Reservations: Only on Tuesday nights.
Parking: Spacious.

The Lodge Restaurant

U.S. Hwy. 59 at State Hwy. 44,
   three miles west of town
Freer
(512) 394-7819
Owner: Ruth Manges
Manager: Ruthie Manges

When you step into The Lodge Restaurant, you wouldn't be at all surprised to see J. R. and his family seated in the big, cushioned dining chairs, enjoying their steaks. The Ewings would feel right at home here, because this handsome, sprawling restaurant set out in the middle of the Texas Brush Country personifies all that is Texas quality, comfort, and design. No detail has been missed, from the mounted deer heads to specially designed etched and stained glass windows where sunset filters through figures of quail, armadillos, a windmill, a pumpjack, and other ranchland symbols. Here and there in the decor the bowlegged *M* of the Manges Ranch appears.

Unless you're a deer hunter or someone with business in South Texas, you might not find yourself passing through the Freer region. However, you *could* be going down for the Corraling of the Coyotes in February or the April Rattlesnake Roundup, and if you're near Alice or Laredo, a drive over to The Lodge for dinner or Sunday buffet will be well worth the time.

The menu is appropriately sumptuous. It ranges from the best steaks to be had to brace of quail, broiled lobster tail, and Alaskan King Crab. The chef teams eye of rib with either quail, shrimp, lobster tail, or baked chicken, whichever you prefer. A welcome alterna-

Your drive to The Lodge, located in the heart of the Border rangeland will be rewarded with gourmet food served in a casually elegant setting.

tive to baked or fried potatoes is the succulent wild rice. For their new restaurant, the Mangeses hired Chef Albert Bencivenga who came to The Lodge from the Army-Navy Country Club in Washington, D.C.

You will probably be greeted at the door by attractive Ruthie Manges, who will answer any of your questions about the family restaurant with both knowledge and pride. She also had a hand in the beautiful decor.

For any of your out-of-state guests with notions that Texas dining may lack taste and elegance even out in the rangeland, The Lodge is the perfect place to bring them to dispel all doubts.

Serving hours: 5 p.m.–10 p.m. Tuesday through Saturday; 11:30 a.m.–
   2:30 p.m. Sundays.
Closed: Mondays, Easter, Thanksgiving, Christmas Eve, Christmas Day.
Dinner, Sunday noon buffet.
Cost of average meal: Expensive.
Special plates and prices: Hamburger for children, half portions of any
   entree for half price.
Credit cards accepted: American Express, Visa, MasterCard, Diners
   Club, Carte Blanche. Only local personal checks accepted.
Special occasion services: Free dessert with candle for birthday. Free
   bottle of champagne for anniversay.
Wheelchair accommdations: Front steps but front door wide enough.
   Restrooms.
Reservations requested on weekends.
Parking: Spacious.

Ludwig's Garden

Not long ago, an Austin restaurateur lamented his feeling that the family-owned restaurant is fast disappearing, that the fast food and other restaurant chains are driving them out of business. Well, that won't happen if there continue to be young, vigorous newcomers to the business such as Larry and Sandra Anderwald.

In 1979, they could obtain only a one-year lease from the owners of a 1930s home on a busy Harlingen thoroughfare. They knew it was the ideal location for a restaurant. Converting the old home to a restaurant entirely with their own hands, their energy and ideas were rewarded with almost instant success. In 1983 they opened a second Ludwig's in McAllen with Larry's brother and sister-in-law, David and Vicky Anderwald, in charge.

The charm of Harlingen's Ludwig's is the decor; the reason you will try to return sometime is the food. If you approach from the front, you'll think you're parking in front of someone's neat, grey and white home with the most perfectly-tended lawn you've ever seen. More parking is around back. Inside, you'll find a homey, almost quaint setting with fresh flowers and brass candle lamps on the tables and an unusual fabric ceiling in the front dining room. The service is friendly and efficient, offering a fresh glass of tea instead of a simple refill whenever you near the end of the one you're drinking.

501 S. 77 Sunshine Strip
Harlingen
(512) 425-1082
Other location: 5401 N. 10th,
   McAllen
(512) 687-7789
Owners: Larry and Sandra
   Anderwald

Winter Texans, natives, and tourists seek out Ludwig's Garden for its food served in a charming former home in Harlingen

The luncheon menu uses eye-catching names such as "Ludwig's Semi-Famous Sausage" in a hot sandwich and "Ludwig's Two-Footer—Serves four starving Tasmanian devils or 1,321,642 German fire ants." The chicken fried steak is ribeye, mind you, so no more of those remarks about this being a fancy way to serve a cheap cut of meat.

The Sunday noon menu, served only during the winter months, December through April by Valley calendars, offers seafood, steaks, sandwiches, and several house specialties. The "Winter Texans," those visitors from the northern states who fill the Valley with their campers and mobile homes during cold weather back home, especially like the baked redfish and Ludwig's northern, grain-fed beef. A house specialty at Sunday lunch is peppered shrimp—fresh Gulf shrimp, sauteed in butter and freshly ground black pepper, served over a bed of wild rice.

For dinner, if you have the Prime Rib Oscar, you will never again allow anyone to criticize Texas food. It is a choice, boneless eye of the rib, topped with crab, asparagus spears, and hollandaise sauce.

Ludwig's thoughtfully provides the official Diet Center plate, and for those of you who don't count calories, an array of homemade desserts will catch your eye. Sour cream apple pie and pecan pie are two of the most outstanding.

There's a good wine list, a low sound level, easy listening music, and guests at neighboring tables who, you can tell, have been here before. You'll quickly understand why.

Serving hours: 11 a.m.–10 p.m. Monday through Saturday; 11 a.m.–3
  p.m. Sunday during the winter months (Dec.–April).
Closed: New Year's Day, Easter, July Fourth, Thanksgiving, Christmas
  Eve, Christmas Day.
Lunch, dinner, and afternoon snacks.
Cost of average meal: Lunch—inexpensive; dinner—moderate to
  expensive.
Special plates: Official Diet Center plate
Credit cards accepted: American Express, Visa, MasterCard. Personal
  checks accepted.
Special occasion services: Pie and candle and the crew sings.
Wheelchair accommodations: Front door.
Reservations suggested.
Parking: Limited.

The Executive Steak House

1500 N. 23rd at Pecan
McAllen
(512) 686-5541
Owner: Gary Della Croce

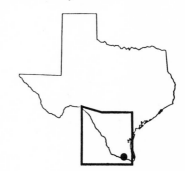

If you're driving what has been called the world's longest Main
Street, forty-three miles from Mission to Harlingen, you're going to
be so lulled by the soft Gulf breezes over Texas' "Magic Valley" that
deciding where to stop to eat won't be easy. Before you realize you
have passed Mission, you're in McAllen, but the numbered streets
make finding The Executive Steak House relatively simple.

Owner Gary Della Croce is a second-generation restaurateur who
revealed the reasons behind his restaurant's popularity in his answer
to one of the questions put to all of the restaurant owners represented
in this book: "What is a special food or service in which you take
pride or for which you are well-known?"

Gary's answer was "Consistently good food and good, friendly service." And that is exactly what you will find here.

At The Executive, no one will *ever* ask, "Is it soup yet?" Their soups
are always rich and flavory and unforgettable. The cream of cheese is
a good example. Our waitress suggested we try the potato and
cheese next time.

A nice substitute for the usual baked potato is listed simply as "another vegetable." Ours was a side dish of cauliflower, cooked to ten-
der-crisp perfection and bathed in real butter.

The "Winter Texans," retirees from colder regions who seek the
warm Valley climate during the cooler months back home, also appreciate the reduced adult portions, which, in addition to prime rib,
include fried chicken, jumbo shrimp, and trout.

The recently remodeled restaurant is a subtly lighted, quiet setting
for a meal guaranteed to be one you will happily remember. Whether
you're an out-of-state visitor, a native Texan, or a new resident, take
time to look at the large collection of fine western prints on the walls
by artist G. Harvey of Austin.

Serving hours: 11:30 a.m.–2 p.m. Monday through Friday; 5 p.m.–10 p.m. Monday through Saturday (5:30 p.m.–10:30 p.m. Summer DST months).
Closed: Sundays, New Year's Day, Thanksgiving, Christmas Day.
Lunch and dinner.
Cost of average meal: Lunch—Inexpensive; dinner—moderate to expensive.
Credit cards accepted: American Express, Visa, MasterCard, Diners Club. Personal checks accepted.
Special occasion services: Cakes for birthdays and anniversaries.
Wheelchair accommodations: Front door and restrooms.
Parking: Limited.

The Round-Up Restaurant

709 U.S. Hwy. 83 W.
Pharr
(512) 787-0842
Owner: Mrs. Otila Garza

The sign out front reads "Round-Up Drive In" and "Round-Up #1 Restaurant." Inside, the decor is Spanish with unexpected crystal chandeliers. The menu features a Spanish waiter on the front and lists most of its selections in Spanish with English translations. If all of this is a bit confusing at first, a newcomer soon ties it all together. Originally, The Round-Up *was* a drive-in. When the food became so popular, expansion was the only answer and so it became a restaurant, with a Round-Up #2 in Harlingen and La Parrilla (the grill), operated by a member of the same family of owners, in Edinburg. And you'll agree that most of the population of the Rio Grande Valley and the Border appear to have been "rounded up" for a meal. The restaurant is crowded almost all of the time, I am told.

In a restaurant in this part of Texas one of the many pleasures of eating any Mexican dish containing guacamole is that the avocados used are always fresh and not overly ripe, as is so often the case in Mexican restaurants farther north and west in the state. The Round-Up's nachos come in several guises, including a topping of tomatoes, onions jalapeños, and guacamole. An absolutely perfect Mexican-seafood combination entree features enchiladas filled with king crabmeat and topped with white cheese, a "special sauce," and guacamole.

Seafood appears again in a soup with a beef stock base. A large bowl is all you will need for a lunch. When strangers at neighboring tables insist you try it, and you learn that they eat here regularly, driving forty miles to do so, you understand. It is succulent and unforgettable!

The house specialty in entrees is their fajitas (beef skirts), marinated and seasoned delicately with Mexican spices. For under twenty dollars, you can order a "Family Platter" for three or four persons, which contains fajitas, guacamole, tostadas, beans, jalapeños, tomatoes, and onions. No one will go away hungry.

You can have American, Mexican, or imported beer, served in huge goblets. They'll even bring your hot or cold tea to you, sweetened or unsweetened.

The meals are so filling that you won't see many people enjoying one of The Round-Up's desserts, but if you can manage it, try either flan, that rich, creamy Mexican custard, or sopaipillas, airy little pastries to be filled with honey and enjoyed.

Serving hours: 11 a.m.–11 p.m. Monday through Thursday, every week of the year; 11 a.m.–12 p.m. Friday and Saturday, every week of the year.
Lunch and dinner.
Cost of average meal: Moderate.
Credit cards accepted: American Express, Visa, MasterCard, Diners Club. Local personal checks accepted.
Wheelchair accommodations: Front door and restrooms.
Parking: Spacious.

Caro's

205 N. Garcia, one-half block off Second St.
Rio Grande City
(512) 487-2255
Owners: Juan and Carmen Caro

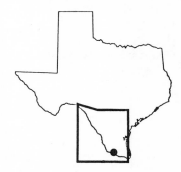

If finding wonderful little off-the-beaten-path restaurants located in unlikely places is your kind of fun, you will *love* going to Caro's. Not that it is really so hard to find. Rio Grande City has two, very long, through streets, each of them one-way. Just head west on Second Street until you reach the cemetery on your left, and you will see a prominent sign, high on your right, directing you to turn here to reach Caro's.

North Garcia Street is wide enough for two cars to pass but not carelessly. Take a window table and you can look across the narrow lane at all the typical Valley colors: yellows and reds, the bright pink of bougainvillaea, and the white of the Spanish olive. A healthy stand of cactus grows midst all this tropical flowering to add further confirmation that this is indeed the Texas Border.

Caro's has been in continuous operation in Rio Grande City for over forty years. A stunning portrait of Juan's mother hangs behind the cash register. It was she who created the light, puffed tostadas for which the restaurant is so well-known. They are a bit like sopaipillas but they are used in place of the tostadas used by many other restaurants serving Mexican food. The guacamole salad comes with the little triangular puffs, and they also provide the shells for tacos. You can also order them as appetizers, filled with guacamole, beef, or chicken. For a good sampling of most everything on the menu, order Caro's "Special Dinner."

The rice is also unique, cooked in chicken broth and seasoned with oregano, cumin, bell peppers, onions, and other distinctive spices. If you've ever passed up rice on a Mexican restaurant menu, don't at Caro's.

Special plates for children feature a wide choice of all the dishes offered on the regular dinners, at reduced prices.

If you need to use the restroom in Caro's, you should know that the six-foot long rattlesnake displayed over the doors is harmless—now.

Juan received a college degree in agriculture in Wisconsin, hoping at one time to become a teacher. Undoubtedly he would have been a fine one, but his dedication to the profession of restaurateuring is one of which he can be proud. His quiet charm and the presence of both him and his wife Carmen exemplify many years of pride in a family business.

Serving hours: 11 a.m.–2 p.m., 5 p.m.–9 p.m. Monday through
    Saturday; 3 p.m.–9 p.m. Sundays.
Closed: New Year's Day, Thanksgiving, Christmas Day.
Lunch and dinner.
Cost of average meal: Inexpensive.
No credit cards accepted. Personal checks accepted.
Wheelchair accommodations: Front door.
Parking: Limited.

The Tin Lizzie Restaurant

107 W. South, one block from
    U.S. Hwys. 83 and 90
Uvalde
(512) 278-2271
Owners: Bob and Sandra
    Keeton

The location of a restaurant has little to do with the tastiness of the food, and certainly a nice setting and atmosphere do not necessarily make a good restaurant. One restaurant in Uvalde, however, has it all. Much of the town's activity still centers around its four plaza squares where some of the surrounding buildings date back to the turn of the century. One of these is the home of the Tin Lizzie Restaurant and Deli, housed in the building where Henry Ford's Model T was first displayed for sale.

The pressed, black tin ceiling remains the same, and the old wood floor still shows the stains of oil, grease, and cigar burns. Here, Ford's cars sold for $850, and gasoline for them cost only twelve cents a gallon. Bob and Sandra Keeton have continued the automotive theme in the restaurant, and at the same time have given the place an attractive period feel, with wood tones, stained glass and ceiling fans.

Even if the restaurant were not so interesting for its original use and present decor, the food would still be delectable and the servings sumptuous. Homemade soups include zucchini, vegetable, chicken noodle, tortilla, and broccoli. The latter is a subtle melding of flavors from minced carrots, onions, celery, and broccoli, along with melted cheese "and lots of other goodies," Sandra says. If you have never

The Tin Lizzie Restaurant is housed in Uvalde's first Ford automobile agency.

tried tortilla soup, do, especially if you are not from the Southwest. It will become one of your best memories of this region.

Appetizers include nachos and fried mushrooms and a new version of the somewhat recently popular potato skins—"Mexiskins," which are fried potato skins covered with seasoned ground beef and melted cheese.

For lunch, a number of light offerings include soup and salad, chicken salad (homemade, of course) and a large chef salad. All sandwich orders are served with a cup of soup of the day. "The Tin Lizzie" is a combination, club-style sandwich with three kinds of meats and two kinds of cheeses. The menu promises it will "melt in your mouth," and it's a promise you can count on. Another choice is "The Model T," a sourdough bread sandwich filled with bacon, tomato, and three kinds of melted cheese, and topped with guacamole and jalapeños. The marinated brisket sandwich contains copious amounts of beef, topped with tomato, guacamole, and jalapeño with a marinade sauce. Succulent and wonderful!

Dinner entrees include steak and jumbo fried shrimp which the Keetons buy fresh, then shell, boil, bread, and cook themselves. Other choices are frog legs, marinated sirloin bits, chicken bits, and hot pepper steak.

For young diners, there are choices of a "Bonnie and Clyde Burger" or a grilled cheese sandwich, both served on granola bread, or chicken bits with cream gravy and french fries.

It's kind of regrettable that cars don't still need cranking to get them started because that's the kind of exercise you're going to need after a Tin Lizzie dessert. All restaurateurs like to tell you their cheesecake is the best in the entire world, but who wants to argue before even testing it? So order a wedge, dribbled with either strawberries or blueberries and pecans. It is so rich and solid you almost have to cut it with a knife, and you won't have the least inclination to question the Keetons on the merits of their cheesecake.

Serving hours: 11 a.m.–2 p.m., 5 p.m.–9 p.m. Monday through
   Saturday.
Closed: Sundays, New Year's Day, Thanksgiving, Christmas Eve,
   Christmas Day.
Lunch and dinner.
Cost of average meal: Inexpensive to moderate.
Credit cards accepted: Visa and MasterCard. Personal checks accepted.
Special occasion services: All birthday honorees get free dessert of their
   choice.
Wheelchair accommodations: Front door.
Reservations requested for more than six.
Parking: Spacious.

Vasquez Restaurant

601 W. Main (U.S. Hwy. 90 W)
Uvalde
(512) 278-5112
Owner: Enrique L. Vasques
Manager: Candelaria S. Luna

   If there is anything you ever wanted to know about armadillos or
the legend-in-its-own-time Terlingua chili cook-off, gregarious restaurateur Enrique Vasquez will be more than happy to tell you about
them and probably a few things you hadn't gotten around to won-
dering about. Vasquez is known for his ability to make armadillos
perform and race and for his involvement as a judge at the renowned
chili cook-off and he likes to talk about both. He will also take time to
make you feel welcome, to chat with guests who are also friends, and
to tell a parting diner, "My love to your wife and children, and drive
carefully!"
   Vasquez Restaurant, whose place mat reminds you it is the "Home
of the Armadillo Chili King," is rightfully proud of its menu, and in a

The Vasquez Restaurant offers seventeen different menu combinations of Mexican food.

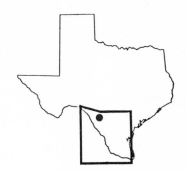

place where modesty isn't exactly the keynote, the pride is fitting. Everything is good, and there are seventeen different combinations of Mexican food items. One is the "Tampiqueña Mexican Dinner," which includes two cheese enchiladas with gravy, top sirloin, refried beans, rice, guacamole, and "Mexican Sauce Ranchera."

A child's plate features a cheese enchilada or beef crisp taco, Spanish rice, and beans, or a ground sirloin patty with french fries.

Steaks and seafood are also served, and several of the steaks are prepared Mexican style. All the servings are generous and reasonably priced.

It's unlikely you will leave feeling any way but pleased that you stopped in, and if you have any doubts about the quality of the food, the sign outside reminds you that the restaurant is "Recommended by Enrique."

Serving hours: 11 a.m.–2:30 p.m., 5 p.m.–9 p.m. seven days a week
Closed: New Year's Day, Easter, July Fourth, Thanksgiving, Christmas Eve, Christmas Day.
Lunch and dinner.
Cost of average meal: Inexpensive.
No credit cards accepted. Local personal checks accepted.
Wheelchair accommodations: Front door.
Special required dress: "Not formal but very proper."
Parking: Spacious.

Nowhere in Texas is the slower pace of Southwestern life more evident than in the small border towns of the Rio Grande Valley. In the restaurants, the waitresses smile at you and take special care to serve you quickly and smoothly; the owner or manager takes time to be hospitable. A guest at a nearby table may ask you where you're from since so many tourists pass through, but also because in Texas such sociable gestures are part of the way of life. At Martha's Kitchen you're in the location of the Valley's chamber of commerce, so townsfolk are especially friendly, but you get the feeling they would be even if hospitality weren't one of the major products here.

This unpretentious little restaurant has become popular with local diners and travelers alike because it offers a broad selection of simple home cooking as well as Border foods. Daily specials include barbecued chicken, catfish, chicken fried steak, pork chops, and a "build your own" Mexican dinner. They call their nachos "Martitas," and they are colorful and a little more elaborate than most you will find. The tostadas are covered with melted cheese, chopped onions and tomatoes, and jalapeños.

Martha's Kitchen

803 S. Bridge at 8th
Weslaco
(512) 968-3232
Owner: Susan Coonrod

Breakfast, lunch, and dinner are served, and there is almost no time you won't find Martha's open. Serving hours are from 6:30 a.m. until 10 p.m. seven days a week, except for Sundays when they close at 2 p.m.

All the pies are baked by Mrs. Snyder in the kitchen and the choices include banana, coconut, chess, chocolate, butterscotch, and pineapple. Susan Coonrod, the pretty owner/manager, in speaking of their pies, borrows a phase from a famous vineyard commercial: "We will sell no pie after its time"—meaning simply, they won't serve day-old pie. Some days hot cinnamon rolls are also available.

Serving hours: 6:30 a.m.–10 p.m. seven days a week 26:30 a.m.–2 p.m.
    Sundays.
Closed: New Year's Day, Thanksgiving, Christmas Day.
Breakfast, lunch, dinner, and afternoon snacks.
Cost of average meal: Breakfast and lunch—inexpensive;
    dinner—moderate.
Special plates: Smaller lunch and dinner with fish or chicken fried steak,
    one vegetable and salad.
Credit cards accepted: Visa, MasterCard. Only local personal checks
    accepted.
Wheelchair accommodations: Front door.
Parking: Spacious.

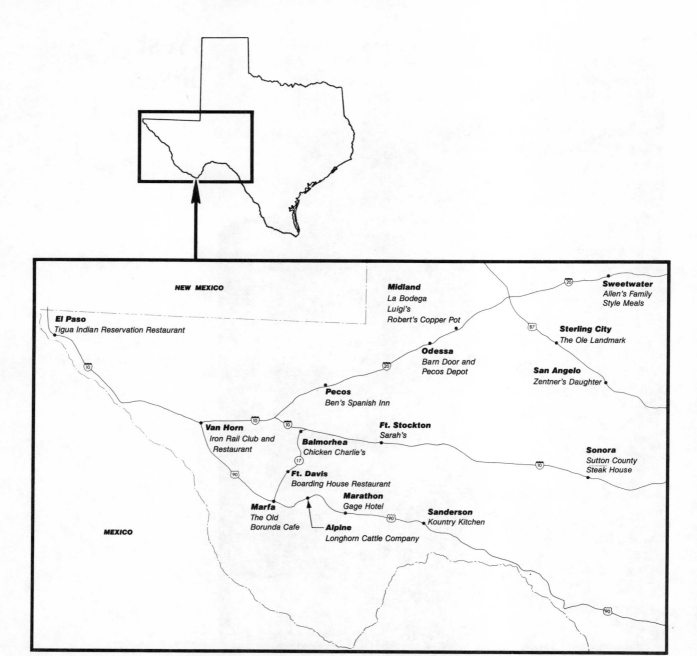

NEW MEXICO

El Paso
Tigua Indian Reservation Restaurant

Midland
La Bodega
Luigi's
Robert's Copper Pot

Odessa
Barn Door and
Pecos Depot

Sweetwater
Allen's Family
Style Meals

Sterling City
The Ole Landmark

San Angelo
Zentner's Daughter

Pecos
Ben's Spanish Inn

Van Horn
Iron Rail Club and
Restaurant

Balmorhea
Chicken Charlie's

Ft. Stockton
Sarah's

Sonora
Sutton County
Steak House

Ft. Davis
Boarding House Restaurant

Marfa
The Old
Borunda Cafe

Marathon
Gage Hotel

Alpine
Longhorn Cattle Company

Sanderson
Kountry Kitchen

MEXICO

Since Alpine is located in Texas' largest county, Brewster County, which is larger than the combined sizes of Connecticut and Rhode Island, it isn't surprising to find a real Texas-style restaurant serving some of the state's biggest steaks. At the Longhorn Cattle Company Restaurant, you can order a thirty-two ounce, family-style sirloin, a sixteen-ounce ribeye, a sixteen-ounce K.C. strip, or a ten-ounce filet. A smaller, six-ounce filet comes with four shrimp. Then, of course, you can count on a good chicken fried steak or chicken strips with gravy.

Owner John Holmes learned how to cut meat on his dad's ranch and taught himself how to cook it. Like some other restaurateurs, John warns you what to expect when you tell him how you want it cooked: "rare" means a red, cold center; "medium rare" will be a steak cooked throughout; but be prepared if you say "well done," because, according to John and many other chefs, your steak will have "no juice left."

Probably more popular even than his steaks is the "Longhorn Burger," drenched in a smoky sauce John created. Appropriate side dishes include potato salad, beans, and jalapeños.

John is a talented photographer, and his color photos of Big Bend National Park to the south remind the visitor how close he is to some of Texas' most spectacular scenery.

Serving hours: 11 a.m.–2 p.m. Tuesday through Saturday; 5:30 p.m.–9 p.m. Tuesday through Sunday.
Closed: Mondays, Thanksgiving, Christmas Eve, Christmas Day.
Lunch and dinner.
Cost of average meal: Moderate.
Special plates and prices: Sandwiches and charbroiled hamburgers for children, 10% discount for senior citizens.
Credit cards accepted: Visa, MasterCard. Only local checks accepted.
Wheelchair accommodations: Front door and restrooms.
Parking: Spacious.

Longhorn Cattle Company Restaurant

State Hwy. 118 N.
Alpine
(915) 837-3692
Owners: John and Donna
  Holmes

While you wait for your chicken fried steak or hamburger, you won't find yourself with nothing to do at Chicken Charlie's. While you won't be able to take it all in from your table, you'll find yourself wrapped in nostalgic reminders of life as it was in the Southwest past. On the walls, on the stairs, on shelves, in corners, and hanging from the ceiling are uncountable pieces of western memorabilia: cattle brands, hats, farming tools, a mounted sheep head from this region, and quite a few things you probably won't be able to name. But when the food comes, your viewing will end.

Chicken Charlie's

Just off I-10
Balmorhea
(915) 375-2433
Owners: Art and Connie
  Climer

You'll be surrounded by western memorabilia too numerous to count at Chicken Charlie's where diners from all over West Texas drive to eat chicken fried steak and homemade pies.

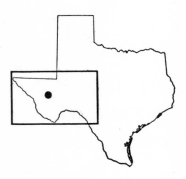

If you've been sampling the *chile macho* salsa on the table, you'll be ready for the quart-size Mason jar of iced tea. If you ordered the chicken fried steak for which Art Climer is famous, you'd better be ready for it. The two pieces of steak are each the size of your hand, covered with cream gravy, served with an enormous pile of french fries and salad, all on a platter large enough to hold a family's Sunday roast. With all this you also get fluffy rolls and a crock of butter. On Sundays only, a smaller plate of chicken fried steak and all the trimmings is available.

You will have selected this feast from a menu written on school children's tablets which also list other choices named after Art and Connie's friends. An example is "Weinacht's Ranch—Named after my friend who I have the honor of doing lots of cooking for, lousy gambler, good Aggie." This item is an eighteen-ounce charbroiled hamburger steak with fries and salad.

Every day there is a choice of pies made by Mrs. Cecil Kingston, a former ranch wife who learned her skill cooking on her ranch near Balmorhea. She cooks exclusively for Chicken Charlie's, and she doesn't give away her recipes, ladies. You wouldn't either if you could prepare them as she does: apple, chocolate, cherry, coconut, and pecan pies, with strawberry pie on Sundays.

Art is a gracious host, willing to show anyone around his place, most of which he built, literally, with his own hands. Most of the interior timber is old, acquired from the Balmorhea depot, high-wire electricity poles, and old buildings. The long bar in "The Roost" was made from these poles. Here and there the original adobe structure has been allowed to show. Upstairs Art will show you a cozy dining room where photos of Midland oil men who are his friends and frequent guests gaze down from the walls. There is also an attractive gift shop upstairs, managed by Connie Climer.

Travelers in RV's will find a small trailer park next door, an unusually pleasant laundromat, a car wash, and picnic tables.

Serving hours: 7 a.m.–10 p.m. Sunday through Thursday; 7 a.m.–2
   p.m. and 5:30 p.m.–10:30 p.m. Friday and Saturday.
Breakfast, lunch, and dinner.
Cost of average meal: Inexpensive to moderate.
Credit cards accepted: Visa. Personal checks accepted.
Wheelchair accommodations: Front door, restrooms.
Reservations: Friday and Saturday nights.
Parking: Spacious.

The Tigua Indians of Ysleta del Sur Pueblo are the oldest identifiable ethnic group in the state. They were settled at their present site
by the Spanish in 1681. In the mid-1960s, they were recognized as a
Texas Indian Tribe by Governor John Connally and as an American
(Federal) Indian tribe by President Lyndon Johnson.

Today, the Tiguas live in the modern pueblo on the southern edge
of El Paso where they produce pottery, jewelry, beadwork, weaving,
and woodwork and operate a unique restaurant. What began as a cafeteria has been converted into a beautiful eating place, featuring subdued Indian decor, comfortable seating, and spectacular Indian,
American, and Mexican food.

Manager Vince Munoz, Jr., points out that all the dishes are made
with fresh-daily ingredients. You won't have to be convinced, once
you taste any of the attractively-served items. When one of the first
items listed is described as "Green Chile, the hottest item on the
menu, jalapeño hot," be grateful for their honesty, and *believe* them.
One salsa is called *pico de gallo* ("rooster beak") and is appropriately
served in stone bowls so thick and heavy, it's a wonder the nice
young Tigua waitresses can carry them. "Salsa diablo" means just
what the name suggests, so any food carrying this description should
also be treated with respect.

The "Caldo de Res" is a shortrib soup and contains potatoes, cabbage, carrots, and the restaurant's own "secret ingredients." It is
served with rice and warm corn tortillas.

One of the most popular entrees is fajitas. These are marinated
strips of sirloin and onions, served on a skillet so hot, it not only is
sizzling when it is brought to the table but the skillet has warped its
wooden serving base. Another marvelous combination of Mexican
and Indian cuisine is the "Pueblo Taco," a huge, Indian fried bread,

Tigua Indian Reservation Restaurant

*Avenue of the Americas Exit off
   I-10*
El Paso
(915) 859-3917
*Owners: The Tigua Indian
   Tribe*

A must for anyone new to Texas or anyone unaware of its existence, the Tigua Indian Arts and Crafts Center and Restaurant offers unrivaled combinations of Indian, Mexican, and American foods.

topped with ground beef and topped again with lettuce, tomatoes, and cheese.

Either before your meal or afterwards, you will surely want to stroll through the bright shopping area adjoining the restaurant. Here you can purchase Tigua paintings, sculpture, jewelry, and freshly-baked Indian bread. The bread is baked just outside in hornos (outdoor ovens) just as Indians have done for centuries. You can also take a guided or self-guided tour through the outdoor area and watch the Tiguas working at their crafts, gardening, or dancing. The dances are scheduled only on certain days, so you had better check before coming if you want to be sure to see them.

If you're new to Texas or traveling this region for the first time, or if you're one of many Texans who had not heard of this one-of-a-kind restaurant and cultural center, don't miss it. The 1682 mission adjoins the arts and crafts complex and restaurant. All are a beautiful blending of the best of both the past and the present.

Serving hours: 9:30 a.m.–4:30 p.m. daily; 9:30 a.m.–8 p.m. Fridays only.
Closed: New Year's Day, Easter, Christmas Eve, Christmas Day.
Breakfast and lunch.
Cost of average meal: Inexpensive.
Credit cards accepted: American Express, Visa, MasterCard, Diners
    Club, Carte Blanche. Local personal checks accepted.
Special occasion services: Birthday cake.
Wheelchair accommodations: Front door and restrooms.
Parking: Spacious.

People who came to Fort Davis early in this century came for the clear air and invigorating climate rather than for chicken fried steak and homemade pies. Today, the Limpia Hotel where they stayed is restored and welcoming travelers again, while its Boarding House Restaurant draws Davis Mountain residents along with a steady stream of vacationers.

The restaurant has a relaxed, family atmosphere where strangers are inclined to exchange greetings and conversation, and waiters are unusually friendly, even for Texas. At breakfast, diners chat among themselves. If they are hotel guests, they may enjoy a continental breakfast of coffee, which is especially good, along with a sweet roll, English muffin, or toast, and cereal. If you're not a breakfast-eater, you might enjoy one of the restaurant's "Fruit Smoothies," blackberry or strawberry, made with yogurt, apple juice, a banana, and frozen strawberries or blackberries.

For lunch or dinner, the choices range from steaks to pork chops with the Boarding House's chicken fried steak an old favorite with customers who come back regularly. Sandwiches, a salad bar, and unrivaled Country Kitchen homemade pies with flaky crusts and some with real whipped cream topping are among the other menu selections.

In warm weather you can sit outside and enjoy a steak cooked on the pleasant patio behind the restaurant. Drinks are available from the Sutler's Club Loft above the dining room. The name *sutler* appears frequently around the restaurant after the early military post storekeepers who were bound to "keep on hand" all the necessities a soldier might need.

After a meal, you might want to visit the beautifully restored Fort Davis down the road or stroll around the corner of the picturesque courthouse square and peek into the Limpia Hotel, the antique-filled bank, or the old general store that still sells supplies to area ranchers.

The Boarding House Restaurant

State Hwy. 17 behind the
*   Limpia Hotel*
Fort Davis
(915) 426-3241
Owners: Mac and Judy Sproul

The Boarding House Restaurant is located behind the Limpia Hotel and down the road from Fort Davis, both restored and open to visitors.

Serving hours: 7 a.m.–9:30 p.m. daily.
Closed: New Year's Day, Christmas Day, December 26.
Breakfast, lunch, and dinner.
Cost of average meal: Inexpensive.
No credit cards accepted. Personal checks accepted.
Special occasion services: Cater group tours, host receptions in hotel.
Wheelchair accommodations: Front door.
Special required dress: "Sloppy dress undesirable. Gentlemen remove hats."
Reservations: During holiday times and summer whenever possible.
Parking: Spacious.

Sarah's

*106 S. Nelson south of
Dickinson (U.S. Hwy. 290),
one block west of Main
Fort Stockton
(915) 336-7124
Owners: Mike and Cleo Castelo*

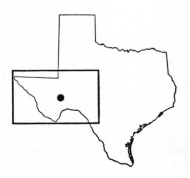

Whether you judge a restaurant by the number of pickups or police cars outside or by the fact that the Class of '73 of Fort Stockton High School fills the tables during their class reunion, Sarah's will pass your test even before you eat. These diners grew up on Sarah Nunez's authentic Mexican food, now served by her daughter and son-in-law, Cleo and Mike Castelo. Sarah opened the restaurant in 1929, and Cleo's long association with good Mexican cooking shows today.

At Sarah's the tostadas are made in the restaurant's kitchen fresh daily, and the tortillas come equally fresh from the commercial kitchen across the street, the Comanche Tortilla Factory.

One of the antijitos (appetizers) such as a burrito with beans or meat, or a smothered burrito with meat, guacamole, sauce, and cheese may be filling enough for a light lunch.

Newcomers to Mexican food might enjoy "Cleo's Special" or "Sarah's Special." Both plates have a good variety of the restaurant's best. If identifying the items is important to you, you'll have to do some uncovering of them under the melted cheese. "Cleo's Special" includes two green enchiladas (green sauce) with sour cream, one taco, rice, beans, and salad. "Sarah's Special" features one enchilada, one taco, one chile relleno (green Mexican pepper), one chalupa, guacamole, and beans. Big flour tortillas, which must be ordered separately, are served in a little straw basket with a Mexican sombrero lid.

Several kinds of beer are available, including ones from Mexico.

Serving hours: 11:30 a.m.–2 p.m. Sundays; 5 p.m.–9 p.m. daily.
Closed: July Fourth, Christmas Day.
Lunch and dinner.
Cost of average meal: Inexpensive.
No credit cards accepted. Personal checks with identification accepted.
Special plates: For children, a plate of ground beef with rice and beans or a taco with rice and beans.
Wheelchair accommodations: Front door.
Parking: Spacious.

Fifty-eight miles south of Fort Stockton and thirty-one miles east of Alpine sits tiny Marathon on the northern approach to Big Bend country. The Gage Hotel there was built in 1927 by Vermont-born Alfred Gage, who had made his fortune in business and ranching in Texas. He felt the Marathon area could use a way station for ranchers like himself to use as an operation headquarters as they traveled to and from their ranches and wherever they called home. (You have to remember the size of some Texas ranches in those days and the limitations of travel and overnight accommodations.) Thus the Gage served as a then-elegant hotel for many years before it closed. Recently it was restored and today offers travelers through the Big Bend region a nostalgic setting for an overnight stay or a meal during a brief stopover.

Gage Hotel Restaurant

U.S. Hwy. 90
Marathon
(915) 386-4588
Owners: J. P. and Mary Jon
*   Bryan*

The Gage Hotel and Restaurant still reflects the relaxed atmosphere of 1927 when it was built as a stopover for traveling ranchers.

While you wait for your meal, you may be joined by friendly guests who have just driven the thirty-one miles from Alpine, as many frequently do, just to eat at the Gage. A busload of tourists may stop off for coffee. Local cowboys may be sitting at a nearby table discussing cattle the same as cowboys did back in the twenties and thirties in this same dining room.

The menu changes daily with a delectable selection to please any taste. An outstanding Mexican plate is featured, along with T-bone steak, grilled chicken, chicken fried steak, chicken and dumplings, and, on weekends, roast duck, smoked prime rib, and shrimp.

Owner Bryan stresses that the Gage is meant to be a family place where attentive service in both the hotel and the restaurant make each guest feel special.

A large menu is available for breakfast, beginning at 7 a.m. Even if you aren't able to stay overnight, ask to see one of the rooms, furnished in hand-made western furniture. You'll want to come back for perhaps a romantic winter weekend, maybe to stay in the room where Zane Grey spent a month writing.

If you have time after dinner, you can sit in the rocking chairs out on the front porch and watch the train go by across the road. The atmosphere of Marathon and the Gage is that relaxing.

Serving hours: 7 a.m.–2 p.m., 5:30 p.m.–9 p.m. seven days a week,
    every day of the year.
Breakfast, lunch, and dinner.
Cost of average meal: Moderate.
Credit cards accepted: Visa, MasterCard. Personal checks accepted.
Special occasion services: Almost anything upon request.
Wheelchair accommodations: Front door.
Parking: Spacious.

The Old Borunda Cafe

203 E. San Antonio St.
Marfa
(915) 729-4338
Owner: Carolina B. Humphries
Manager: Stephanie Spitzer

For ninety-six years this legendary restaurant has been in operation, in this building since 1910. Carolina Borunda Humphries has operated it "only" since 1938. She keeps declaring she is going to close, and it is true that on some days she doesn't open, so you had better call ahead to be sure if she is going to.

You will sit in a smallish room in which everything is sparkling white—the floor, the booths, the tables and chairs, even the refrigerator back near the kitchen. The tables and chairs are the kind in which you may have sat, eating your Wheaties and drinking Ovaltine out of a Little Orphan Annie Shakeup Mug, if you are old enough to recall such breakfast memories.

Don't be in a hurry when you go, because Carolina moves slowly these days, and you can watch her through the kitchen door, pains-

The Old Borunda is one of the oldest home-owned restaurants in the state operated by the same owner, Carolina Borunda Humphries.

takingly preparing each plate. Occasionally, she opens the door of her big, 1897 woodstove on which she cooks everything, and feeds the fire another stick of mesquite. (She keeps food warm on a gas stove nearby but claims that gas "cooks too fast and ruins the food.")

There is nothing to nibble on while you wait. Carolina doesn't even serve tostadas or tortillas with her meals, because she would have to buy them, ready-made, and this goes against her principles. So you'll get plain white bread with your meal. But the food . . . ah, *this* is "the real thing." Ask her about her secret, about the seasonings, etc. "I don't use any," she'll tell you. Question the delicate balance of flavors. She'll laugh modestly and tell you "That's because the food is made by a Spanish girl!"

This wonderful "Spanish girl" has some precise if slightly ambiguous regulations about the consumption of alcohol within her restaurant. A sign over the kitchen door reads: "Only two beers per customer with each meal. No intoxicating liquors permitted at any time!" Translation: You may bring your own beer—but only two. And no wine nor any other alcoholic beverage is allowed.

The menu contains all the standard Mexican fare: enchiladas, chicken and beef tacos, nachos, tamales, chile con carne, beans, guacamole. Try some of it all.

You can order the traditional Mexican dessert, homemade pralines. Better take along some extras for later nibbling. Like all good Mexican food, one bite is never enough.

There are some restaurants to which people return year after year or again after many years' absence. At The Old Borunda, two groups of diners were overheard as they discovered each other's presence. They hadn't seen each other in forty years. The Old Borunda is the kind of place you want to visit again. You had better hurry.

Serving hours: 5:30 p.m.–8:30 p.m. Monday through Saturday.
Closed: Sundays, July Fourth, Christmas Eve, Christmas Day, and some
    other days.
Dinner only.
Cost of average meal: Inexpensive.
No credit cards accepted. Local checks accepted.
Wheelchair accommodations: Front door.
Parking: Spacious.
Special attraction in which we take pride: "Our friends."
No alcohol served.

La Bodega

2700 N. Big Spring
Midland
(915) 684-5594
Other locations: 7th and Dixie,
   Odessa, (915) 333-4460
   Ave. Q and 22nd, Lubbock,
   (806) 747-1361
Owner: Alois Munzer

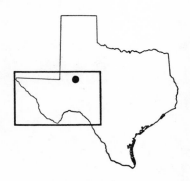

You have probably noticed that the Midland home-owned restaurants in this book are all located on N. Big Spring, which is also State Highway 349, which runs north and south through the city. If you are a traveler, you will discover these are easy-to-find locations. Should you ask any Midlander which Midland restaurant has the best Mexican food and most beautiful setting combined, you're sure to be told "La Bodega." It is often the special occasion choice of kitchen-weary housewives, Midlanders entertaining out-of-town guests, and young couples who enjoy the fountains and flowers, candlelight and unobtrusive service.

La Bodega is so popular, there is often a wait before your meal, but architect Frank Welch, who designed the restaurant, provided a relaxing balcony lounge where you can have a drink and perhaps an order of nachos while you wait for your table. The sky-lighted restaurant is so comfortable, unless you're in a tremendous hurry, you won't mind the delay. Looking down from the walls are photographs from the Mexican Revolution, some featuring the infamous Pancho Villa. The bar is open until 2 a.m., with nachos available until midnight.

Regular guests all have their favorites, and among them is the "La Bodega Salad," which includes tacos and guacamole but becomes a full meal when ordered with the enchilada. Another favorite is the rueda, a sort of Mexican pizza, which is actually a flour tortilla covered with your choice of chicken, ground beef, or shrimp; beans; a rich tomato sauce; melted cheese; and sour cream. If fiery flavors don't bother you, you'll find the chiles rellenos delicious with their garnishes of pecans, raisins, and sour cream.

Midland's La Bodega provides a romantic setting for superior Mexican food.

La Bodega is also known for its use of seafood in Mexican dishes. "Vera Cruz Style Red Fish" is a local favorite, along with "Shrimp a la Mexicana," served with rice and guacamole.

Like the other restaurants chosen for this book, La Bodega has built a reputation for diligent owner interest and involvement. The tall, handsome gentleman you see strolling about is owner Alois Munzer, a European-trained chef who learned Mexican cooking from a leading Austin restaurateur. His constant attention to his guests' satisfaction is one of the main reasons for the restaurant's steady success.

La Bodega means *wine cellar* in Spanish. It also means superb Mexican food in beautiful surroundings.

Serving hours: 11 a.m.–10 p.m. Monday, Wednesday through Sunday.
Closed: Tuesdays, New Year's Day, Easter, Thanksgiving, Christmas Eve, Christmas Day.
Lunch, dinner, afternoon and late night snacks.
Cost of average meal: Moderate.
Special plates: Children's plates.
Credit cards accepted: Visa and MasterCard. Personal checks with identification accepted.
Wheelchair accommodations: Front door.
Parking: Spacious.

Luigi's Italian Restaurant

111 N. Big Spring, downtown Midland
(915) 683-6363
Owners: Louis and Zelda Hochman

If they left Luigi's front door open and let all those warm, Italian aromas float onto the street, they'd probably have to erect barricades to control the crowd. As it is, salivating throngs of diners have been flowing into Luigi's for over twenty-five years. Lou and Zelda Hochman are community-involved Midlanders who know everything there is to know about running a successful restaurant, and it takes only a minute for a newcomer to realize it.

The spacious dining area still manages a feeling of intimacy, with red and white-checkered table cloths and candlelight. The walls reflect the Hochmans' support of the Midland Community Theatre and the Midland Jazz Festival, with photographs of professional and local performers attractively displayed. Unobtrusive plaques and certifi-

Lou and Zelda Hochman have been serving some of the best Italian food in West Texas—maybe in the whole state—for 25 years at Luigi's Italian Restaurant in Midland. Photo courtesy of Bruce Partain.

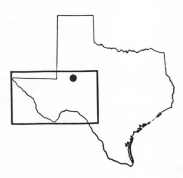

cates acknowledge Lou's activities in community organizations and the Texas Restaurant Association. The atmosphere of the room is quiet, the service superb, and there is no better Italian food anywhere in West Texas, maybe not in the entire state.

Midlanders return for favorites such as Luigi's baked lasagna, which can be ordered with a dinner salad and could satisfy the appetite of a traveler who hasn't eaten since he left El Paso. Eggplant Parmigiana is served with a side order of spaghetti or a dinner salad and garlic bread. Some Midlanders swear by the cannelloni, tender egg noodles with beef and pork, whole milk ricotta, mozzarella cheese, and imported Romano cheese, baked in a choice of white or red sauce. Then there's Veal Parmigiana and other selections for bigger appetites, but for something lighter, you might want to try the hot pastrami sandwich, the small or large antipasto salad, generously heaped with cheese, or one of the many pizzas which come with every conceivable topping combination.

Special children's plates are available, and these same plates are offered to senior citizens at the same prices. If you can resist the lure of the surrounding fragrances, you can order a "Slim and Trim" salad with julienne chicken breast, a hard-boiled egg, and tomato wedges. Takeout food can be ready in an incredibly short time if you call ahead. The small adjoining bar offers a wide selection of mixed drinks and wines.

One of the features which sets Luigi's apart from any other Italian restaurant anywhere is the ethnic mixture of the personnel, especially appreciated by local diners. Cook Joe Reyes has been with the restaurant for twenty years. Jerry Perkins, the amiable black dishwasher, has been an employee for fifteen years. And three weeks after opening, Lou Hochman attracted national press attention when he placed a simple local newspaper ad which announced that he would be closed from sundown to sundown on Yom Kippur. A sign near the cash register reads "Se Habla Yiddish."

Serving hours: 11 a.m.–10 p.m. Monday through Saturday.
Closed: Sundays, New Year's Day, Memorial Day, July Fourth, Labor
    Day, Christmas Day, Yom Kippur.
Lunch and dinner.
Cost of average meal: Moderate.
Credit cards accepted: American Express, Visa, MasterCard. No
    personal checks accepted.
Special occasion services: Champagne for birthdays or anniversaries.
Wheelchair accommodations: Front door.
Parking: Limited during the day, spacious at night.

Robert's Copper Pot

*Wadley and N. Big Spring in
    Claydesta National Bank
Midland
(915) 684-9862
Owners: Bob and Bettye
    Conklin*

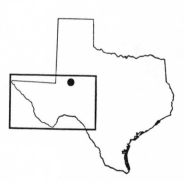

When you step into the eclectic decor of Robert's Copper Pot for the first time, right away you'll understand why they call it "a dilly of a deli." Bob and Bettye Conklin have filled their casually intimate little restaurant with an unusual assortment of eye-catchers: a stuffed mountain lion on top of the telephone booth, an authentic green turtle decoy from the Cayman Islands, flags, paper parasols, photographs, and, of course, lots of copper pots.

Don't be surprised to be greeted and have your hand shaken by genial Bob who will know your name the next time you drop by. "Customers expect to be noticed" is the Conklins' philosophy toward their guests, and it has made the Copper Pot one of the most popular eating places in Midland.

At noon, the restaurant is crowded with oil business professionals, local media people, volunteers working over at Midland Community Theatre, and frequent out-of-town manufacturers' representatives who have heard about the restaurant from other salesmen. Evenings, the tables may be filled with parents and their children, retired couples, college students, and young singles. The comfortable closeness of the tables, combined with the restaurant's English pub-like atmosphere, provide a setting for Texas camaraderie at its best.

Bettye is one of the most innovative cooks in West Texas. Many of the recipes served at the Copper Pot are in her cookbook which is for sale. Specials often include "Hot as Hades Chili" (believe it!), Caribbean black bean soup, gazpacho, stuffed jalapeños, gumbo, and pinto bean soup.

The hot sandwiches are among the most popular items. Try the crispy "Monte Cristo," a deep-fried confection of a small French loaf filled with ham, turkey, and Swiss cheese. Or the cold "Mufaletto," an Italian sandwich feast on a sourdough French bun, crammed with smoked ham, provolone cheese, salami, black olives, lettuce, tomatoes, and a spicy Italian sauce. Locals return for lox, cream cheese, and bagels and cold weather specialties such as stew and meat loaf. Desserts include baklava and several kinds of cheese cake.

The Copper Pot serves the largest selection of imported beers in West Texas as well as a good choice of wines. Carry-out trays can be prepared for travelers in RV's, autos, or private aircraft.

Serving hours: 11:30 a.m.–9 p.m. Monday through Saturday.
Closed: Sundays, New Year's Day, July Fourth, Thanksgiving, Christmas Day.
Lunch, dinner, and afternoon snacks.
Cost of average meal: Inexpensive to moderate.
Credit cards accepted: American Express, Visa, MasterCard. Only local, approved personal checks accepted.
Special occasion services: Candle in cheesecake or "almost anything you want."
Wheelchair accommodations: Front door and restrooms.
Parking: Spacious.

The Barn Door and Pecos Depot

23rd and N. Grant (U.S. Hwy. 385)
Odessa
(915) 337-4142
Owner: Frank Green

Regardless of how you approach this sprawling West Texas city, looking at its spare skyline and sparse outskirts, you might doubt that good eating is to be found there. Finding The Barn Door and Pecos Depot will change your mind. If you're coming from either east or west on Interstate 20, you need to know that U.S. 385 is the same as the Andrews Highway and the same as N. Grant, which is the city's Main Street. You'll have an easy, straight route to Frank Green's popular restaurant from any direction.

Forty-seven years in the restaurant business shows in every detail of the restaurant, which Green has operated for over fifteen years. The tall, lean restaurateur greets guests with Texas friendliness, looking much like many of his western-dressed diners. He is a big supporter of the Texas Restaurant Association, and The Barn Door reflects all that organization represents.

In the restaurant, you can eat in one of three dining rooms: The Barn Room, filled with western antiques, the Gay Nineties Room, or the Gold Room. A full menu is offered in these rooms. In the adjoining Pecos Depot, which serves as a bar, homemade soups and buffet sandwiches are served at noon.

The depot is a must for exploring and is sure to excite railroad buffs. Built in 1892, it was eventually bought by the Santa Fe Railroad until it was declared surplus because of declining railroad business. Green bought and restored it, and now the ticket offices, waiting rooms, and freight room serve as dining and sitting rooms filled mostly with authentic antique furniture. It's a relaxing Victorian setting for a drink or for lunch.

All meals come with a complimentary bowl or cup of soup—homemade and delicious. The soups are different each day and include

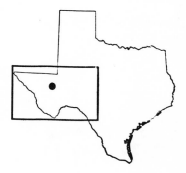

vegetable, macaroni and tomato, okra and rice, cream of potato, and chicken noodle. All the breads are also homemade, and you'll be tempted to fill up on the hot loaf served with a block of cheese before your dinner.

Steak and seafood are the specialties here, and you won't be disappointed in any choice. A platter-size slice of roast prime rib au jus is offered for a luncheon special with thicker cuts also available. Seven steak selections include a large Texas T-bone, pepper steak, and a small tenderloin. You can also team your steak with shrimp, chicken filets, or enchiladas.

The butterfly shrimp are worth writing home about on one of the Barn Door's souvenir post cards. Even on this West Texas prairie so far from deep fishing waters, you can still have good shrimp, oysters, and crab. Naturally, catfish is also listed on the menu.

You can enjoy any of a nice selection of Mexican dinners and separate dishes including chimichangas, which are flour tortillas filled with beef, sour cream, and guacamole.

The snappy service is further evidence that owner Green knows how to run a restaurant. All the waitresses appear to be experienced, and all are eager to please. I asked one how much chicken-fried steak is served here, and she replied that "it's mostly ordered by the cowboys." For anyone new in these parts, the men dressed as "cowboys" are mostly oil patch workers. According to my waitress, it's the diners in ties and jackets who order the prime rib and K.C. strips. (They may be oil patch workers, too.)

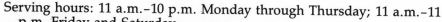

Serving hours: 11 a.m.–10 p.m. Monday through Thursday; 11 a.m.–11 p.m. Friday and Saturday.
Closed: Sundays, Christmas Day.
Lunch and dinner.
Cost of average meal: Moderate.
Special plates: Dieters' specials daily, children's menu.
Credit cards accepted: American Express, Visa, MasterCard, Diners Club, Carte Blanche. No personal checks accepted.
Special occasion services: Birthday and anniversary cakes.
Wheelchair accommodations: Front door and restrooms.
Reservations requested.
Parking: Spacious.

Ben's Spanish Inn

815 W. 3rd (U.S. Hwy. 80)
Pecos
(915) 445-4383
Owner: Ben Matta

For a lot of people, good Mexican food satisfies a craving not unlike seeing the Cowboys win. Writer Alison Cook goes so far as to call it "nursery food," "those dishes we turn to for comfort in times of adversity." No matter what your state of mind or situation, the food at Ben's Spanish Inn will both satisfy and comfort.

More than forty years ago the Matta family began serving enchiladas, tacos, chiles rellenos, and other Mexican dishes that have made their restaurant as popular in West Texas as Pecos cantaloupes. At noontime and dinner, the dining rooms are filled with local diners, and travelers on I-20 who have taken a good look at the map often plan a stop in Pecos before continuing any farther.

The noon buffet offers all you can eat of an array of every Mexican dish you can dream of: both red and green enchiladas, Frito pie, chiles rellenos, refried beans, tacos, Spanish rice. All for under four dollars. A la carte you can order both American and Mexican meals, some them named after well-known Pecosites. Warning: Here's that salsa called "pico de gallo" again. Bear in mind that means "rooster beak" in Spanish. If you like it hot, dig in.

Three thoughtful plates *para los ninos* are listed for children under ten only. They include a Mexican plate, a chicken strip with french fries, rice, and a salad, and a hamburger patty, french fries, a roll, and salad.

The only time you may have a little wait for service or in line for the noon buffet is during the July Fourth annual Pecos Rodeo and Old Timers Reunion. But if you want to see some real West Texans, you couldn't be in Pecos at a better time.

Serving hours: 11 a.m.–2 p.m., 5 p.m.–10 p.m. Monday through
    Saturday.
Closed: Sundays, New Year's Day, Christmas Day.
Lunch and dinner.
Cost of average meal: Inexpensive.
Special plates: Children's plates.
Credit cards accepted: Visa, MasterCard. Local personal checks
    accepted.
Wheelchair accommodations: Front door and restrooms.
Parking: Spacious.

Any West Texas restaurant with the name Zentner means steaks. Good steaks. In San Angelo, Zentner's Daughter Steak House is one of several family-owned restaurants owing their existence to John Zentner, who probably knows more about good steaks than anyone in West Texas. His knowledge goes all the way back to World War I when he worked as a butcher and cook in the Army. Since that time, he has run restaurants, ranched, sold cattle, and helped his daughters open their own restaurants in San Angelo.

When you ask Zentner what makes a good restaurant, he doesn't hestitate a minute. "Good meat. But it has to age properly, a week to ten days."

Betty Zentner calls her father "the boss," but her touch and that of her husband Richard are very much around in their steak house. The western decor is attractive, service is efficient and quick, and the steaks have naturally been "aged properly" and perfectly cooked. The restaurant boasts "the largest steaks in West Texas" and serves them to probably the largest number of diners at one time than any other Texas steak house.

Other menu selections are available besides steaks: fish, sandwiches, even a diet plate. But ordering fish at a Zentner's would be like having spaghetti in Singapore.

Be sure to look at photograph near the entrance. John Zentner is smiling out on his guests with a contented look of satisfaction. After your meal there, you'll understand why.

Serving hours: 11 a.m.–2 p.m., 5 p.m.–11 p.m Tuesday through Sunday.
Closed: Mondays, Thanksgiving, Christmas Day.
Lunch and dinner.
Cost of average meal: Moderate.
Credit cards accepted: American Express, MasterCard, Diner's Club.
   Personal checks accepted.
Special plates: Child's plate, senior citizen discount, Tuesday–Friday
   noon special.
Wheelchair accommodations: Front door and restrooms.
Special required dress: Shirt, shoes.
Parking: Spacious.

Zentner's Daughter Steak House

*1901 Knickerbocker Rd. S., off
  U.S. Hwy. 87
San Angelo
(915) 949-2821
Owners: Richard and Betty
  Zentner Easingwood*

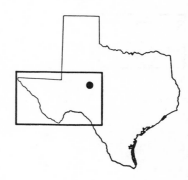

In West Texas, the name Zentner means good steaks, especially in a restaurant run by one of John Zentner's daughters.

Kountry Kitchen

305 W. Oak (U.S. Hwy. 90)
Sanderson
(915) 345-2581
Owner: Goldie Brown

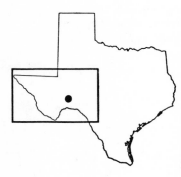

Fifty-four miles due east of Marathon, Sanderson is a comparative metropolis with a population of roughly 1,300. Since it is practically the only town of *any* size in all of Terrell County, it is the undisputed hub of activity for this part of the Border. If there was anyone in Sanderson who wasn't eating at the Kountry Kitchen on the rainy day I dropped in, he must have been out of town. Everyone in Terrell County seemed to have sought shelter for the enjoyment of one of Goldie Brown's good lunches. Other out-of-town visitors included a busload of touring Waco retirees. School bands and football teams are frequent stopover diners, Goldie said.

People seem to take a kind of perverse pleasure in remembering disasters which have befallen their communities. If there has ever been a hurricane, a flood, fire, or any other memorable calamity in a town, you can be sure some of the restaurant owners will display a photographic record along the walls to show visitors just how bad it was. In Sanderson it was the big flood of July 1965 when twenty-one lives were lost. So naturally, this rainy day conversation at tables occupied by townspeople occasionally touched on memories of that tragedy. Since it was hunting season, there was also talk among the men about white-tail deer spottings.

The Waco folks all ordered separately, so when time came for them to go, there was a goodly lineup at the cash register. But the Kountry Kitchen is such a friendly place and patience being the key word, service to other tables slowed only a mite, and no one got ruffled. You get the feeling that the tone of this little restaurant is always like this, pleasant and relaxed, except maybe during a flood.

Goldie came to the restaurant business with some of the best possible training. For many years she cooked for roundup crews on her family's ranch. Now, with help from two sons and a daughter, she prepares the same kind of simple, country cooking which is still in demand for breakfast, lunch, and dinner.

The menu covers just about every regional dish anyone could want in this part of Texas. For breakfast selections include such things as "Kountry Boy Special"—three pancakes, two eggs with ham, bacon or sausage, "good coffee", syrup and butter. Each listing of coffee included in the price assures you it will be "good coffee." You can also order pork chops and eggs, a Spanish omelette, or biscuits and gravy.

Lunch and dinner offer you a wide choice, including chicken fried steak, barbecue plates, Mexican food, steaks, veal cutlets, and sandwiches. Goldie's two most popular desserts are peach cobbler and bread pudding, but she says quite a few of her guests tell her she should just cook peach cobbler, and they could all quit arguing over which one is better. The debate must liven up even more on days she adds her homemade pies, doughnuts, cinnamon rolls, and apple fritters.

The Kountry Kitchen is an ideal traveler's stopover. Sitting amid all that homey atmosphere, surrounded by red-and-white checked, ruffly curtains, red-and-white checked table cloths, and red-and-white costumed waitresses so eager to please, you'll be reluctant to head on for Langtry or Del Rio or wherever. But you won't find any better food anywhere along the way.

Serving hours: 6:30 a.m.–9 p.m. Monday through Friday; 8:30 a.m.–9
  p.m. Sundays; 11:30 a.m.–2 p.m. Sunday buffet.
Closed: Saturdays, New Year's Day, July 16–31, Christmas Day.
Breakfast, lunch, and dinner.
Cost of average meal: Inexpensive.
Special plates and prices: Senior citizen's or child's plate with half
  orders of chicken fried steak, veal cutlets, pork chops, fried chicken or
  hamburger steak.
No credit cards accepted. Personal checks accepted.
Special occasion services: Set up for special parties in separate room,
  furnish menu of your choice.
Wheelchair accommodations: Front door.
Reservations preferred for large groups.
Parking: Spacious.

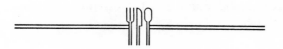

Sutton County Steak House

I-10 and Golf Course Road
Sonora
(915) 387-3833
Owners: Preston and Linda
  Love

Sutton County is ranching country, primarily in sheep and goats.
Many ranchers lease their property for turkey and deer hunting. At
the Sutton County Steak House, Preston and Linda Love have provided the ideal restaurant for local ranchers, visiting hunters, Sonora
residents, and travelers through this part of the Edwards Plateau. In
one dining area, light filters through large stained glass panels which
Linda designed from photographs of the area, showing colorful
scenes of hunting, ranching, and oil production, another focus of
Sonora activity.

To know who eats regularly at a restaurant is to know how successful it is, and the Steak House is a good example. It is the favorite eating place for the Independent Cattlemen's Association, oil company
safety meetings, the Sonora Lions Club, area football teams, and local
cowboys and oilfield roughnecks. But if you're a tourist just passing through, you'll feel equally at home. It's that kind of place.

One of the special attractions is the excellent service. Another is the
freshness and the amount of meat in each serving in which the Loves
take well-deserved pride. When they list a "Large T-Bone" on the
menu, they aren't just kidding around. It will weigh thirty-four
ounces. Their "Texas-sized Hamburger" weighs twelve to fourteen
ounces. Possibly the best item on the menu is a plate of what they call
"Steak Bits." These are trimmings from sirloin in bite-sized pieces
cooked to perfection, tender, and filling enough as an entree since
they also come with a salad or soup, and french fries, or a baked potato.

Wednesday nights is barbecued brisket, ribs, and sausage night.
Friday nights the special offering is Mexican food. Naturally, there is
always chicken fried steak. Onion rings are a specialty many returning guests order. If you're under twelve or over sixty-five, three en-

trees at a modest price are a meat patty, tenderloin of trout, and chicken fried steak, served with a salad on the plate, and french fries or a baked potato. The chicken bits are favorites with al ages of diners.

This is a true, family operation. "We're a team," Linda says, and the teamwork is a winner at the Sutton County Steak House. You'll be glad you stopped.

Serving hours: 6 a.m.–2 p.m. Monday through Saturday; 5 p.m.–10
   p.m. Monday through Thursday; 5 p.m.–11 p.m Friday and Saturday.
Closed: Sundays, Christmas Eve, and Christmas Day.
Breakfast, lunch, and dinner.
Cost of average meal: Inexpensive to moderate.
Credit cards accepted: American Express, Visa, and MasterCard. No
   out-of-town personal checks.
Special occasion services: Birthday cakes.
Wheelchair accommodations: Front door and restrooms.
Parking: Spacious.

The Ole Landmark

U.S. Hwy. 87
Sterling City
(915) 378-7981
Owners: Bob and Nadine Hicks

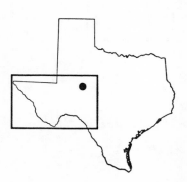

Bob and Nadine Hicks are Sterling City residents who, with typical West Texas vigor, run both a restaurant and an oil company. When Bob gave Nadine two buffaloes as a present, the buffalo became the logo for their company, JATAM. Naturally, it also became the logo of The Ole Landmark.

The menu satisfies the appetites of both the many oil field workers who eat there as well as the gourmet tastes of other guests. Chef Carolyn Hunter prepares or supervises the dishes, many of which are original creations. You may be tempted to fill up on the homemade breads and forget to leave room for the pastries. The pies could drive all thoughts of food from your mind for miles.

The menu satisfies the appetites of both the many oil field workers who eat there as well as the gourmet tastes of other guests. Chef Carolyn Hunter prepares or supervises the dishes, many of which are Joann's creations. You may be tempted to fill up on the homemade breads and forget to leave room for the pastries. The pies could drive all thoughts of food from your mind for miles.

Hope that catfish is on the menu the day you arrive. They are understandably proud of it. Sunday buffet is popular with five or six vegetables, ten salads, and two desserts. If you're a newcomer to Texas, try Carolyn's homemade chili. You'll never again be satisfied with any which comes out of a can.

An "After Five" menu includes more sophisticated selections, but dress in the After Five dining room is still casual. You can order lob-

The Ole Landmark is a welcome sight to hungry travelers between Midland and San Angelo.

ster or steak Chateaubriand, and perhaps Cherries Jubilee for dessert.

Daily specials cost under five dollars and are a full meal, but you can also order hot or cold sandwiches and salads.

The Ole Landmark isn't a destination restaurant—yet. But Texans think nothing of driving fifty miles or more for a good meal, so it won't be surprising soon to see diners from throughout the Permian Basin who drove all the way from home to Sterling City for a special meal.

Serving hours: 6 a.m.–11 p.m., 11 a.m.–2 p.m., 6 p.m.–9 p.m. Monday through Saturday; 11 a.m.–2 p.m. Sunday noon buffet.
Closed: New Year's Day, July Fourth, Thanksgiving, Christmas Eve, Christmas Day, New Year's Eve at 2 p.m.
Breakfast, lunch, and dinner.
Cost of average meal: Moderate.
Credit cards accepted: American Express, Visa, MasterCard, Diners Club. Local personal checks accepted.
Special occasion services: Cake and candle.
Wheelchair accommodations: Front door.
Parking: Spacious.

If you haven't heard of Allen's, you've never asked anyone in Sweetwater where is the best place to eat. Some people think it's the best family-owned restaurant in all of Texas. Lizzie Allen has been serving lunch to hungry travelers and townfolk alike since 1940. Son Bill, who manages the big, one-room restaurant, says, "When beer went out, Mother went in." "In" is a good word to describe what Allen's has been from the beginning.

Nothing fancy but fantastic food: fried chicken to write home about and always one other meat; eight to ten vegetables, such as okra

Allen's Family Style Meals

1301 E. Broadway
Sweetwater
(915) 235-2060
Owners: Mrs. Lizzie Allen, Bill Allen

Lizzie Allen has become the best-known restaurateur in West Texas, serving family-style meals since 1940.

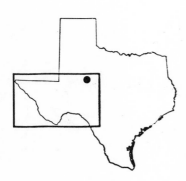

gumbo, sweet potatoes, red beans, squash, corn, and potatoes; three to four salads; marvelous rolls; and just one dessert—exquisite peach cobbler—which you would have chosen anyway if you'd had a choice and had known what to expect. You can order fried chicken to go, and lots of people do.

The only meal served is lunch, but if you're by the restaurant in the evening you may see a crowd across the parking lot in the big building where the Allens cater wedding parties, family reunions, and retirement parties "nearly every night." They cater barbecue parties, too, within a hundred-mile radius of Sweetwater.

You'll get a friendly welcome when you eat there, not just from the Allens but from local diners. (One family invited me to spend the night after I looked over their antique collection at the back of their business nearby.) Everyone sits at long tables, and the meal is served family style. The price is unbelievably reasonable, and when they say, "Come back!" as you leave, you know they mean it, and you do too when you say, "I will!"

Serving hours: 11 a.m.–2 p.m. Tuesday through Sunday.
Closed: Mondays, Mother's Day, Father's Day, Christmas Eve, Christmas Day.
Lunch only.
Cost of average meal: Inexpensive.
No credit cards accepted. Personal checks accepted.
Wheelchair accommodations: Front door.
Parking: Spacious.
No alcohol served.

Strangers to Texas driving Interstate 10 westward towards El Paso sometimes tend to get a little panicky soon after they pass through Pecos. The highway stretches on and on with almost no towns at all, and *both of them* seem to have little visible reason for being there. Then the wayfarers drive into Van Horn where Main Street (old U.S. 80) is lined with motels of every class and description. But why? Who on earth would intentionally drive out to this West Texas desert town, intending to stay overnight? What these travelers don't know is that around Van Horn, white-tailed and mule deer as well as pronghorn antelope attract hunters by the score. And the invigorating climate provides ideal conditions for camping in the nearby foothills and mountains with magnificient views in all directions. They also probably don't know there is a restaurant and private club where they can enjoy eleven- to twelve-ounce ribeye steaks or top sirloin, elegant chicken dishes, fresh vegetables, and great sandwiches.

The Iron Rail Steak House, along with its private club, is a charming place to visit and to quit trying to understand why West Texans *like* endless horizons and skies. Inside the restaurant you can look at all the railroad memorabilia, the antique fireplace, the one-hundred-and-fifty-year-old bar, and the old light fixtures (John will happily tell you all about where he got them), and have a meal to help you convince skeptics that there is indeed "food after Fort Stockton."

You can quench your desert thirst with any of several beers, wines, or one of John's special drinks. His "Medori Margarita" is a melon and honey-flavored margarita that is different and delicious. (On Mondays, if the Cowboys lost, he prepares a special blue marguerita.)

Other entrees that are popular with Van Horn residents and travelers alike include prime rib, chicken Jerusalem, beef stroganoff, and stuffed pork chops. The thoughtful owners also offer some of the menu items in one-half portions for either children or senior citizens.

The Iron Rail Club and Steak House

U.S. Hwy. 80
Van Horn
(915) 283-9902
Owners: John and Vicky Jones

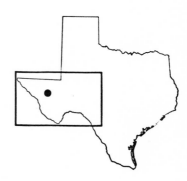

The Iron Rail Restaurant proves that there is "food after Fort Stockton"—delicious food.

Order at least one of the special vegetables: the three-cheese potato, sauteed mushrooms, fried mushrooms, zucchini, cauliflower, okra, or the asparagus.

Among the sandwiches, the "Rail Burger" is six ounces of ground beef, charbroiled on a French roll, with cheese, a chili pepper strip, and sauteed onion added, if you wish.

Vicky's honey-wheat bread is a treat you'll remember. Ask your waitress about the homemade dessert of the day.

When you have to leave and drive on westward, you can talk about the Iron Rail all the way to El Paso. By then you'll be hungry again, so turn to the El Paso entry for some more good eating in West Texas. (It *is* possible to go due north or south from Van Horn if reaching another town anytime soon isn't important to you.)

Serving hours: 6 p.m.–11 p.m. Monday through Saturday.
Closed: Sundays, New Year's Day, Easter, Thanksgiving, Christmas Eve, Christmas Day.
Dinner only.
Cost of average meal: Moderate to expensive.
Credit cards accepted: American Express, Visa, MasterCard, Diners Club, Carte Blanche. Only local personal checks accepted.
Special occasion services: Cake with sufficient notice.
Wheelchair accommodations: Front door and restrooms.
Special required dress: "No dirty, offensive clothing."
Reservations requested for groups over six.
Parking: Spacious.

High
Plains and
Panhandle

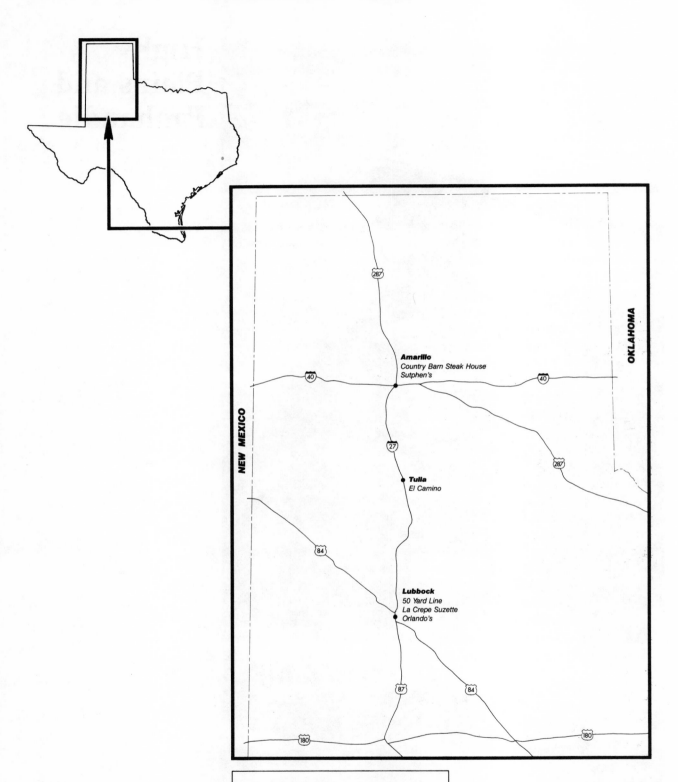

If you don't know what calf or turkey fries are, a waitress at The Country Barn Steak House will politely explain. These Southwestern delicacies are only a small part of the western atmosphere in this spacious restaurant, conveniently located for travelers passing through Amarillo.

The restaurant operation dates back to 1964 when Highway 66 was the main artery connecting East to West. Today, regular customers from the East return, en route to western destinations. Behind the cash register, the wall is filled with photographs of national celebrities who drop by for a good steak or one of the many other menu selections. And some of the best-looking Texans anywhere can be seen dining at the red-and-white-checkered-cloth-covered tables. On Friday and Saturday nights, Amarillo residents crowd the place to eat and dance to the music of a country and western band. Anyone daring to enter without removing a hat or hair curlers will be asked to do so by Norma Marrs, who has old-school ideas about proper dining-out attire. ("*Real* cowboys remove their hats.") Norma says most customers cooperate with her house rule, and even tired truck drivers have been known to freshen up in the restroom before asking for a table.

Norma is joined in the twenty-year-old business by other members of her family: son Donald Marrs, along with daughter and son-in-law Diana and Tommy Pepper.

Norma's husband, the late John Marrs, collected the antiques and western memorabilia which provide the restaurant its decor. His collection fills the walls and corners. Western art and photographs hang on every wall, including an eye-stopping photo of a triple hanging from some long-past time, some well-worn cowboy gear, mounted steer and buffalo heads, an old still with a lifelike fire glowing underneath, and the end of an old chuck wagon which serves as counter space today. Be sure to step into the Saloon to see more.

Service is superb with waitresses fetchingly dressed in short, red-and-white-checked dresses. A busy crew of young cooks and other employees bustle between the dining room and the spotless, enormous kitchen, where pinto beans are cooked, seventy-five pounds at a time. Wearing white chef hats and uniforms, red neckerchiefs and

The Country Barn Steak House

I-40 East at Lakeside Exit
Amarillo
(806) 335-2325
Owners: Norma Marrs, Donald
*   Marrs, Tommy and Diana*
*   Pepper*

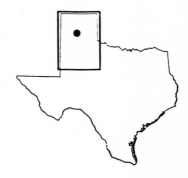

aprons, an attractive lineup of cooks prepare part of the meals in view of diners. Several of the employees have been with the restaurant as long as eighteen years.

For those who may not want to try the calf or turkey fries, the choice of appetizers on the menu lists a homemade soup of the day, shrimp cocktail, and escargots. The restaurant serves the only prime rib in Amarillo, and perfectly-cooked steaks from every cut are available. None of the steaks needs it, but the menu offers a mushroom steak topping, aptly named "The Crowning Glory for Broiled Steaks," made with mushrooms, butter, soy sauce, and Burgundy wine. Other entrees include seafood, catfish, chicken kiev, chicken fried steak, hickory pit barbecue, and a Mexican dinner. If you like, you can finish off with your choice of a tantalizing list of desserts or sip your favorite aperitif.

Serving hours: 11 a.m.–11:30 p.m. Sundays; 5 p.m.–10:45 p.m. daily.
Closed: New Year's Day, Easter, Thanksgiving, Christmas Eve, Christmas Day.
Lunch and dinner.
Cost of average meal: Moderate to expensive.
Credit cards accepted: American Express, Visa, MasterCard, Diners Club, Carte Blanche. Local personal checks and travelers checks accepted.
Special occasion services: Small cakes for birthdays and anniversaries.
Wheelchair accommodations: Front door.
Special required dress: No bare feet nor undershirts, no hair curlers nor hats worn.
Reservations: Accepted anytime but needed for Friday and Saturday nights.
Parking: Spacious.

Sutphen's Barbecue

16th and Madison from Washington Exit on I-40 E.
Amarillo
(806) 373-0726
Other location: 303 N. Cedar, Borger
(806) 273-6442
Owner: Scott Sutphen

Whether at Sutphen's in Amarillo or in Borger, "barbecue plate" takes on new meaning. *Larruping* is the word to describe the mesquite-smoked beef, ribs and sausage, served on a plate heaped with potato salad, cole slaw, and onion rings, with thick Texas Toast, sliced pickles, sweet onions, and stewed apricots on the side. For obvious reasons the Sutphen family takes pride in its two restaurants which have been operating in Amarillo for eighteen years and in Borger, where they first started, for thirty-three.

Diners have a choice of several combinations of the meats. The menu also lists a "Family Style" meal of ribs, beef, sausage, and pork strips and all you can eat of the relish tray, potato salad, cole slaw, beans, onion rings, and Texas Toast. There is a single, "Family Style"

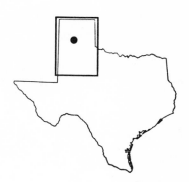

price for adults as well as one for children. In addition to the succulent barbecue, should anyone be able to pass it up, Sutphen's serves hamburgers, chicken fried steak, barbecued chicken, and a chef salad that includes one small barbecued rib. Five selections on the menu are designed for children under ten years of age and customers over sixty-five at a special price.

Casually-clad diners enjoy Sutphen's food seated in the comfortable chairs of the restaurant and line up to sample it also in Palo Duro Canyon before the summer performances of *Texas!* Scott Sutphen, who operates the Amarillo restaurant, will cater local groups or serve his barbecue as far away as Oregon and Washington, D.C. Scott grew up in Borger, where his parents still handle the original restaurant. His interest in his community and his business is reflected in the Amarillo operation.

Some of the employees, both in the kitchen and out front, have been with Sutphen's for as long as eighteen years, and their experience shows in the good service as well as in the quality of the food.

Serving hours: 11 a.m.–9:30 p.m. Monday through Saturday.
Closed: Sundays, Thanksgiving, Christmas.
Lunch and dinner.
Cost of average meal: Moderate.
Credit cards accepted: Visa, MasterCard. No personal checks accepted.
Wheelchair accommodations: Front door.
Reservations: Will accept for large groups.
Parking: Spacious.
Beer, wine.

The 50 Yard Line

11th at Slide in the Redbud
Shopping Center
Lubbock
(806) 793-5050
Owners: Jerrell and Wanda
Price, Don and Jouana
Stravlo

At The 50 Yard Line, football fans can feel they are sitting almost right on the playing field, dining under the larger-than-life-size mural of the Texas Tech Red Raiders in action. The colorful mural stretches the length of the main dining area of the restaurant and is the decor to be expected when one of the owners is Jerrell Price, Tech's first All-American. In this simply-furnished but inviting restaurant, football helmets from both pro and college teams fill the walls in the dining room and in the Press Box Lounge, which also features a wide-screen TV (to better watch televised football, naturally). Bright green Astro-Turf carpet is used throughout the restaurant along with matching green tablecloths. Here the football atmosphere ends because, even with a crowd, the place is pleasantly quiet.

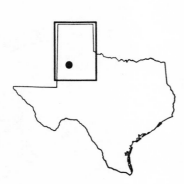

Dress is casual, and week nights attract local diners. The regulars don't hesitate to order their favorites, with thick, juicy steaks cooked perfectly to order heading the list. The menu lineup continues the football theme with steaks named "The Quarterback," an extra cut, 14-ounce ribeye, and "The Linebacker," a 12-ounce prime rib. Smaller cuts are also available, as well as chicken fried steak, broiled flounder, popcorn shrimp, three kinds of nachos, and a basket filled with fresh, homemade cheese rolls and small, delectable blueberry muffins.

Newcomers can expect a crisp, generous relish dish, a cup of hot onion soup, and attentive waiters immediately after being seated. The house dressing for the salad is a sweet-spicy Italian. Special plates for children and weight-watchers are offered at prices lower than those for the average meal.

The 50 Yard Line is an unpretentious and reliable place to eat in Lubbock and certainly worth the easy drive from a highway or across town to its central location.

Serving hours: 5 p.m.–10 p.m. Monday through Thursday; 5 p.m.–11 p.m. Friday and Saturday.
Closed: Sundays, New Year's Day, July Fourth, Labor Day, Thanksgiving, Christmas Eve, Christmas Day.
Dinner only.
Cost of average meal: Moderate.
Credit cards accepted: American Express, Visa, MasterCard, Diners Club.
Personal checks with identification accepted.
Special occasion services: Complimentary cakes for birthdays and anniversaries.
Wheelchair accommodations: Front door and restrooms.
Reservations: For six or more but suggested for Friday and Saturday nights.
Parking: Spacious.

The owners are French. The food is French. The bread is made from French flour by French bakers in Dallas. If it's your birthday, they'll sing "Happy Birthday" to you in French. But if you think French means fancy or pretentious, think again, and have lunch or dinner at this beautiful, low-key restaurant where the owners show visible interest in your dining enjoyment. Larry is in the kitchen preparing the delectable menu selections most of the time, but he will pop out for an introduction if you ask. Marie-Louise will greet you at the door and show you to a table.

The daughter of a French Navy admiral, Marie-Louise learned to cook from the personal chefs assigned to her father during her youth in the south of France. From them she learned how to prepare such entrees as filet mignon, served with a red wine and shallot sauce, and "Le Chateaubriand," broiled tenderloin served with a combination of vegetables and Bernaise sauce.

Crepes come filled with all kinds of mouth-watering ingredients: chicken, spinach, mushrooms, and crab meat with cream and wine sauce. For lunch a Shrimp Louis salad is enough for any size appetite. Lettuce is arranged in bite-sized pieces around a saucer-big tomato heaped with fresh, boiled shrimp; eggs; chopped, fresh green onions; and green bell peppers and sprinkled with fresh parsley and a zesty Louis sauce. The salad is accompanied by thickly-sliced French bread.

Special weekend offerings are the gourmet dinners with entrees such as shrimp quiche, filet of flounder with crab meat stuffing, and for dessert, pineapple, flambéed at your table and served over ice cream. Where French names are used, the menu is thoughtfully translated. For your convenience, a choice of appropriate wines is even suggested.

The wine list itself is a visual treat. The owners have pressed bottle labels between transparent pages of a book with prices listed underneath the labels. Even the hors d'oeuvres menu is accompanied by wine suggestions.

You would be wise to read the desserts offered before you decide on your entree. The chocolate mousse is a favorite, but who could pass by "Le Mont Blanc Chocolate:" "Vanilla ice cream and chewy, crunchy meringue topped with chocolate with a touch of brandy covered with whipped cream"?

The split-level restaurant features stained glass panels, lighted subtly from behind; eye-catching paintings, some by local artists in a rotating exhibit; unobtrusive lighting; and pleasant French music in the background.

La Crepe Suzette

*2420 Broadway, one-half block
from Texas Tech campus
Lubbock
(806) 762-1345
Owners: Lawrence E. and
Marie-Louise Gautreaux*

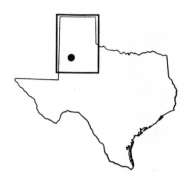

Serving hours: 11:30 a.m.–2 p.m. Monday through Friday; 6:30 p.m.–10 p.m. Monday through Sunday.
Closed: New Year's Day, Memorial Day, July Fourth, Labor Day, Thanksgiving, Christmas Day.
Lunch and dinner.
Cost of average meal: Moderate to expensive.
Credit cards accepted: American Express, Visa, MasterCard. Personal checks accepted if approved by owner before arrival.

Special occasion services: For birthdays, a cake with candles, "Happy Birthday" sung in French.
Wheelchair accommodations: Front door.
Special required dress: Shorts prohibited except for dress shorts at lunch.
Reservations: Will accept but not necessary.
Parking: Spacious.

Orlando's

2402 Q (U.S. Hwy. 84) at 24th
Lubbock
(806) 747-5998
Owners: Loyd and Karen
Turner, Mike and David Cea

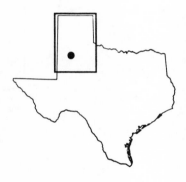

If enthusiastic management, imaginative design, and good food are all the ingredients needed for a popular restaurant, then the owners of Orlando's have the right recipe. Conveniently located on the north-south highway through the edge of downtown Lubbock, the restaurant has been growing steadily in favor with local diners. The minute you step inside, you understand why.

The natural finish of the wood on the bar and walls gleams. Rough cedar posts separate booths where tables are covered, as in the main dining area, with bright red-and-white-checkered tablecloths. Interesting color photographs taken by owner Loyd Turner dot the walls. And in warm weather, fresh, cool air circulates from evaporative, rather than refrigerated, air conditioners.

Since 1965 there has been an Orlando's, but in 1978 Loyd Turner, now with wife Karen, joined the partnership. The industrious carpentry of their friend Morris Fitch transformed the old pizzeria, which started out as a convenience store, into the delightful place it is today.

Customers return for appetizers such as fried zucchini with Orlando's ranch-style dip, mushrooms sauteed in oil, wine, and spices, and, of course, nachos and guacamole. Favorite entrees include spaghetti, lasagna, manicotti, Italian sausage casserole, and deep-dish pizza. Fried shrimp and fried chicken are also listed on the lengthy menu.

Orlando's is no doubt one of the few Italian restaurants anywhere which offers a selection of entrees, sandwiches, and even pizzas, made from all-natural ingredients. These include a chicken and broccoli casserole made with chicken, broccoli, almonds, brown rice, and mozzarella cheese, spiced with the restaurant's "secret seasonings."

Also two all-vegetable and cheese pizzas and "fruit smoothies," made with yogurt; raw, local honey; orange juice; and your choice of fruit are offered. Any of the menu items may be ordered to take out.

Serving hours: 11 a.m.–10 p.m. Monday through Thursday and
  Sunday; 11 a.m.–11 p.m. Friday and Saturday.
Closed: New Year's Day (open at 5 p.m.), Easter, July Fourth,
  Thanksgiving, Christmas Day.
Lunch and dinner.
Cost of average meal: Inexpensive.
Credit cards accepted: American Express, Visa, MasterCard. Personal
  checks with local identification.
Special occasion services: Complimentary champagne for anniversaries,
  a round of drinks for birthdays.
Wheelchair accommodations: Front door.
Reservations: For banquet room parties only.
Parking: Spacious.

No one ever claimed that the stretch of U.S. Highway 87 from Lubbock to Amarillo was scenic or filled with the lure of tourist attractions. But to relieve the flat, grain- and corn-filled landscape, a stop for some of the best Mexican food anywhere is sure to mean a meal to remember.

Gracious El Camino owner Delta Lee has been associated with restaurant operation virtually all of her life, and her experience shows. Daughter Gaye McLendon manages the Tulia restaurant.

Recipes for the menu listings are Delta's own, developed almost twenty years ago when she acquired ownership of El Camino. Her chile rellenos may be the most popular menu item, but area diners return for enchiladas, steak con queso, and any of the large combination dinners for two to six people. She also serves a child's plate of Mexican food, hamburgers, or sandwiches. Fresh, crisp tostadas arrive daily. The menu even provides help with pronunciation of the Spanish names for foods listed. Lunch and dinner are the most often served meals, but breakfast is also available before 11 a.m.

Delta has expanded the restaurant, which was originally a service station, several times. On Sundays a line of hungry guests outside is a common sight. In local polls, Panhandle diners often name El Camino their favorite restaurant for Mexican food. No one who eats Delta's way of preparing it will wonder why.

Serving hours: 11 a.m.–10 p.m. Monday through Sunday.
Closed: Christmas Eve, Christmas Day.
Breakfast, lunch, and dinner.
Cost of average meal: Inexpensive.
No credit cards accepted. Personal checks accepted.
Wheelchair accommodations: Front door and restrooms.
Parking: Spacious.

El Camino

U.S. Hwy. 87 S.
Tulia
(806) 995-4083
Owner: Delta Lee

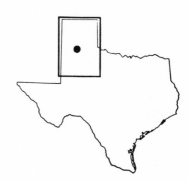

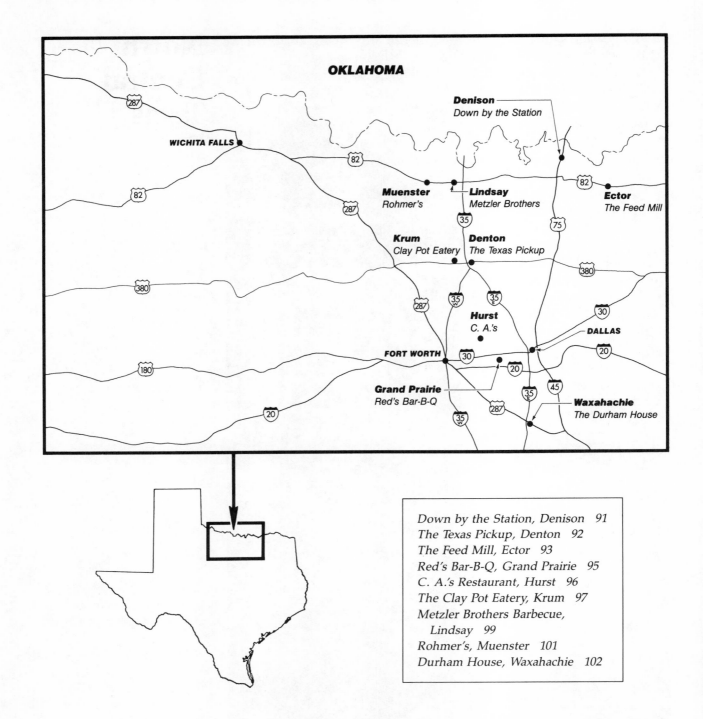

If you possess a gourmet's tastebuds, a romantic heart, an appreciation of the old and the beautiful, and you feel a heart-tug at the sound of a train rattling by, you will adore the Down by the Station Restaurant. It is situated in the Traveler's Hotel, built in 1893 by Ernest Martin Kohl, a former German Navy captain. The first floor was originally a grocery and mercantile store and saloon. In 1908 Kohl began adding the three upper floors for his family's residence. In the 1930s the building became the Traveler's Hotel, drawing business from the nearby railroad district. Today it offers bed and breakfast accommodations in addition to the restaurant.

When you taste any of the Continental specialties on the menu, you will recognize a Cordon Bleu quality and for good reasons. Innkeeper and chef Bob Brandt is a graduate of the Cordon Bleu cooking school and also served as a chef in Dallas' Fairmont Hotel at one time. Everything he prepares reflects his training, and you positively will not be disappointed in anything you select.

An appropriate hors d'oeuvres would be escargots from the Burgundy region of France, baked in their shells with a garlic herb butter and served with hot French bread. Steaks include "Chateaubriand for Two," twenty ounces of center cut tenderloin, grilled to your specifications, and served with the chef's bouquetier of vegetables.

The entrees also include tournedos chasseur, butter-tender, center cut tenderloin, sauteed in butter and topped with hunter sauce. Exquisite! You may also choose from chicken, veal, and pasta dishes prepared as deliciously as any you will ever enjoy. Seafood selections include trout almondine, lobster tail, crab legs, and shrimp.

Down by the Station

*300 E. Main St., in the
    Traveler's Hotel
Denison
(214) 465-2372
Owners: Bob and Betty Brandt*

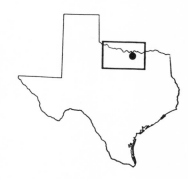

One of the most romantic restaurants in the state is Down by the Station, located in the old Traveler's Hotel.

The salads rest in an old railroad luggage cart which the Brandts converted into a refrigerated unit, blending function with the restaurant's setting.

Children are welcome guests in the restaurant, and a special menu "For the Little Engineers" (twelve years and under) is available. The selections offer chopped sirloin, shrimp, chicken breasts, hamburgers, spaghetti, and a four-ounce filet, and, of course, french fries.

Cheesecake topped with blueberries or cherries needs to be anticipated for a delectable ending to a meal to remember.

The rooms used for lunch and dinner guests are tucked into the first floor areas once used as the mercantile store, the carriage shed, and the wine cellar. Bob cut through two-and-one-half-foot stone walls to carve out an intimate dining nook from the wine cellar. On nearby wall bricks, names and dates of workmen and others are still legible. You will enjoy looking around at all the reminders of the hotel's earliest days: original shelves for merchandise, brass drawer pulls, old stoves, and much more. This is one more restaurant and inn which can easily qualify as one of those Very Special Places.

Serving hours: 11 a.m.–2 p.m. Monday through Thursday; 6 p.m.–10 p.m. Friday and Saturday. Lounge opens at 11 a.m. daily.
Closed: Sundays, New Year's Day, Memorial Day, July Fourth, Labor Day, Thanksgiving, Christmas Eve, Christmas Day.
Lunch and dinner, complimentary continental breakfast for hotel guests.
Cost of average meal: Expensive.
Credit cards accepted: American Express, Visa, MasterCard, Diners Club. No personal checks accepted.
Special occasion services: Any request plus cake.
Wheelchair accommodations: Front door.
Reservations requested.
Parking: Spacious.

The Texas Pickup

Ave. D Exit off I-35 to Ave. E and Prairie
Denton
(817) 382-1221
Owners: Bill and Marion Graham

The name started out to be that of a mixed drink, but although that idea didn't work out, a great little restaurant did. The Texas Pickup is one of those cozy places where you're enfolded by theme decor. You have to do a lot of looking and peering around the rough-hewn walls to see all the gimme caps, old license plates, and the many tire, gasoline, beer and soft drink signs. Sound hokey? It is, a little, but charming and attractive in every detail, a fun place, the perfect setting for the many North Texas State University students it draws, but older diners flock to Bill and Marion Graham's place, too.

The energetic young couple keep service at a swift pace and Bill's dishes coming out of the kitchen with servings so enormous that *calorie* had better not even be a word in your vocabulary when you go there to eat.

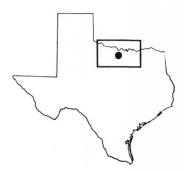

The menu is fashioned after a license plate, and some of the selections follow the automotive theme. "Low Lead" is a dieter's salad, or so they claim, but probably not for anyone really serious about losing weight. It is composed of lettuce, tomato, egg, onions, one-third pound of ground beef, croutons, and cheese. Lots of cheese. The "Chicken Ranch" is also billed for dieters (everything is relative here), so go ahead if you actually think you can lose weight on a plate heaped with fried chicken breast strips with cream gravy on the side for dipping. However, the accompanying salad does, indeed, contain a lot of low-calorie lettuce, along with tomato, egg, onions, and croutons.

But if food is what you're after with no silly thoughts of holding back, go for the "Red Neck Muther" cheeseburger or "Texas Pickup Chili" with a couple of handfuls of cheese on top. The large chicken fried steak dinner ought to hold you for a day or two. The small size should satisfy you at least until the next meal, maybe then some. For a daintier appetite, "Matt's Mexican Special" is a beautiful plate of lettuce, tomatoes, chili, cheese, onions, and Fritos.

There is a special, different soup each day as well as a cobbler of the day. The beverage list includes a good selection of draft and bottled beer.

If you're traveling or want food to go for any reason, the Pickup will prepare anything on the menu in a jiffy.

The restaurant has only been in business since 1976 and is shining proof that if restaurant owners do 85% of everything right, they'll be a success. With the Texas Pickup, make that 100%.

Serving hours: 11 a.m.–2 p.m., 5 p.m–9 p.m. Tuesday through
    Saturday, June through mid-August; 11 a.m.–9 p.m. Tuesday through
    Saturday, mid-August through May.
Closed: Sundays, Mondays, Memorial Day, July Fourth, Labor Day,
    Thanksgiving, Christmas Eve, Christmas Day, New Year's Eve.
Lunch and dinner.
Cost of average meal: Inexpensive.
No credit cards accepted. No personal checks accepted.
No wheelchair accommodations.
Parking: Spacious.

The Feed Mill

One block north of U.S. Hwy.
82 at blinking light
Ector
(214) 961-3355
Owners: Carl and Dolly Stone

Add to the list of locations which didn't start out as restaurants an old feed mill, which before that was a general store, grocery store, and post office during the 1800s. Ector is southeast of Denison, and it will be almost impossible for you not to be able to locate The Feed Mill Restaurant. There is only one blinking light, and north is the direction of the railroad tracks. If you're traveling this part of Texas, stop, or people who *have* will be telling you forever why you should have.

Add to ways to judge the quality of a restaurant before you eat there the fact that the owner is so busy taking orders and greeting guests by name that you know it will be a while before he can sit down with you and visit. Then when you meet Carl Stone's wife, Dolly, you learn that this hard-working pair are so organized and proficient that Carl regularly drives an eighteen-wheeler for a fertilizer company, leaving Dolly to run the restaurant.

In less than five years they have built a reputation for some of the best food in this part of Texas: meat loaf, hamburger steaks, Mexican food, catfish, homemade pies and cakes, and chicken fried steak that *Texas Monthly* described as "large, tender, country-spiced, cream-gravied" and "the best" in the state in their 1980 "Best List." Recently, the Stones added quail to their menu, teamed with shrimp or steak.

It's a casual, leave-your-order, pick-it-up-yourself, help-yourself-to-tea-or-coffee place. You'll sit with customers from the North Texas area, Ector residents, returning travelers, and newcomers who have heard about the Feed Mill, and you'll be able to look around the big dining room with its original floors and brick walls at old feed signs on the walls and, in the center of the room, the original scales. A huge fireplace at one end adds atmosphere during the cold months. On weekends an organist provides entertainment.

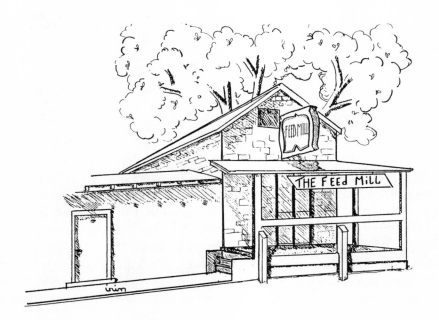

Carl and Dolly have taken special care to ensure their guests' satisfaction. They've set aside one room "just for the school kids." A big door closes to contain their chatter. *Anyone* can order a child's plate at a child's plate price. There are two sizes of chef salads and also a roast beef plate for dieters. "We like to work with dieters to help them out," Carl says. (Incidentally, these are not native Southwesterners. Carl and Dolly are both from New York state.)

On top of all this, there is one prominent calendar from a local business on the wall. That says it all.

Serving hours: 6 a.m.–8 p.m. Tuesday through Saturday; 12 p.m.–3 p.m. Sundays.
Closed: Mondays, New Year's Day, July Fourth, Thanksgiving, last two weeks in December.
Breakfast, lunch, and dinner.
Cost of average meal: Inexpensive.
No credit cards accepted. Personal checks accepted.
Wheelchair accommodations: Front door and restrooms.
Parking: Limited.
No alcohol served.

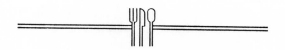

Red's Bar-B-Q

713 E. Jefferson
Grand Prairie
(214) 264-2811 or 262-9154
Owners: Adele Slight, Val
Slight

Even if you arrive the minute Red's Bar-B-Q opens at 11 a.m., you won't be eating alone. Lots of other hungry people in Grand Prairie know when the restaurant opens, and they'll be right behind you. But they won't have to wait long in the cafeteria style serving line because service is smooth and fast. Co-owner/manager Val Slight may prepare your barbecue sandwich or plate. Val is one of many second generation restaurant owners who grew up in the business. Today, he and his mother Adele operate the Grand Prairie restaurant.

He is justifiably proud of many aspects of the restaurant. He recently added barbecued pork (shoulder) to the menu because it is much favored by out-of-state diners. When a Los Angeles firm wanted him to cater a luncheon in Los Angeles, he sent one hundred pounds of his good smokey meats, packed in an ice chest marked with the restaurant's name via a commercial airline carrier. In a few days someone came in and asked what his ice chests were doing in the Los Angeles airport. Val was happy to explain.

U.S. Phantom Jet pilots from nearby Hensley Naval Air Station are frequent guests, and they too carry the word about Red's good barbecue when they move on to other assignments.

You won't mind serving yourself after you pick up your plate of whichever meat you've chosen. There's hardly an edible critter that moves which they don't barbecue here. You can select from turkey, chicken, pork, ham, ribs, sausages, and beef, all served with homemade sauce. Then there is potato salad, cole slaw, barbecued beans, pinto beans, baked potatoes with trimmings; french fries, fried okra, and fried onion rings. Takeout food is quickly prepared.

As you enjoy your meal in the comfortable, rustic dining room, you'll see Red's lunch or dinner guests continually streaming in. But watch how quickly they get through the serving line and sit down to the business of eating some of the best barbecue in Texas. If you're just passing through, you'll be glad you stopped, and it's a cinch you'll spread the word about Red's wherever you're headed.

Serving hours: 11 a.m.–9 p.m. seven days a week.
Closed: Thanksgiving, the week between Christmas and New Year's Day.
Lunch and dinner.
Cost of average meal: Inexpensive.
No credit cards accepted. Personal checks accepted.
No wheelchair accommodations.
Parking: Limited.
No alcohol served.

C. A.'s Restaurant

440 W. Pipeline
Hurst (just east of Fort Worth)
(817) 282-2666
Owners: C. A. Sanford, Paul Sanford

The restaurants selected for this book met certain criteria. They are successful, mostly over a long period of time. They offer both first-rate service and food. (It doesn't *have* to include chicken fried steak in spite of evidence which might suggest otherwise.) The decor, lighting, sound level, etc. are pleasant and unobtrusive. And, perhaps most important, the owners demonstrate *visible* interest in their guests' satisfaction. "Best" lists are, of course, always a matter of opinion, but when you visit C. A.'s Restaurant in Hurst, prepare to agree: they've got it all.

The reason behind this very special restaurant is obvious: C. A. Sanford and son Paul share a zeal for their restaurant and its guests, unrivaled anywhere in the state. If you read the back of the menu or visit with C. A. in person, you'll soon learn he is a man who believes in returning with personal service to his community much of what he has received in the way of business success. He is the current president of the Texas Restaurant Association, the former mayor of Hurst, and sponsor of several large fund-raising golf tournaments to support the search for a cure for cancer. Former employees have gone on to restaurant and other careers as a result of his scholarships. He is much in demand as a humorous public speaker. And this is only a partial list of his activities, although he says, "I don't play as much golf as my customers think I do!"

The attractive restaurant which started out serving only hamburgers in 1962 now serves a wide selection of "Texas Style Eatin'" with chicken fried steaks as the headliner. Some 600 a day, C. A. says. If you can pass up what lots of people testify is the best in the state (served on top of the cream gravy so "you can see what you're getting"), then you can choose from chicken livers, steaks, enchiladas, pork chops, fried shrimp, fried chicken chunks with gravy, and catfish. The fried okra is fabulous, and the cheese-vegetable soup will be a conversation topic wherever you meet someone else who has tried it. C. A. will even give you the recipe. Just ask at the cash register as you leave.

Typical of the restaurant's accommodating services, there is a selection of plates for "The Small Appetite": chicken fried steak, fried chicken livers, country fried pork chop, or jumbo fried shrimp. Three other plates are designed for children.

Don't miss looking around the "Good Times Room" where you can eat or enjoy a drink. It has a family atmosphere and eclectic decor including an antique bar from Scotland, a colorful panel from an old merry-go-round, and beautiful antique musical instruments on the walls.

You may see some well-known personality sitting at a nearby table because C. A.'s is known all over the country as one of the best places to eat outside the cities themselves in the Dallas-Fort Worth area.

The menu is as much fun to read as just looking around and enjoying the restaurant surroundings. One part reads: "If this ain't good eatin', then grits ain't groceries." You said it, C. A.

Serving hours: 11 a.m.–9:30 p.m. Monday through Saturday; 11 a.m.–3
　　p.m. Sunday.
Closed: Christmas Day.
Lunch and dinner.
Cost of average meal: Inexpensive.
Credit cards accepted: American Express, Visa, MasterCard. No
　　personal checks accepted.
Wheelchair accommodations: Front door and restrooms.
Parking: Spacious.

The producers of *Dallas* thought The Clay Pot Eatery so interesting that, with a few alterations here and there, they used it for an episode of the TV series. If they could seek out Krum and find it, you can too, and you'll be happy that you did. It's just west of Denton, and if it were forty miles instead of four, the drive would still be worth what lies at the end.

Talk about a family operation! Hal, husband of Phyllis and father of Michael, Steve, Vicki, and Sandra, probably has the most enjoyable, and certainly the easiest, job. He greets guests as they enter and ac-

The Clay Pot Eatery

Four miles from I-35 Krum Exit
Krum (west of Denton)
(817) 482-3927
Owners: The Miller family:
　Hal, Phyllis, Michael, Vicki,
　and Sandra

The Clay Pot Eatery is easy to find and boasts probably the largest and best salad buffet in the state.

cepts their praise and thank-you's as they leave. Phyllis designed and decorated the restaurant and now serves as cook and organizer. Steve and Michael help out when they can, and Vicki and Sandra work full time in the kitchen, preparing the incredibly good dishes The Clay Pot has become famous for.

Soups and salads vary from day to day, but all are culinary wonders. Ladies, imagine the biggest and best salad luncheon you ever attended, and you'll have some idea of the selection. "Salad bar" takes on new meaning here. I counted more than twenty-five salads for lunch, excluding the basic green with all its many garnishes (baby white corn, two kinds of olives, watermelon rind pickles) and all the gelatin salads. The twenty-five included green tomatoes, cucumbers, green peppers and other good things, sweet and sour broccoli, curried rice, barbecue-flavored (yes) rice, plus others gorgeous to look at, impossible to identify at one sitting but marvelous to eat. Hal explained that on Saturday nights the number of choices is "much bigger." That is the night he makes the potato chips, potato skins with cheese and bacon bits, corn fritters, and other hot and tasty items. A welcome convenience is the dishes guests are given—no flat, slippery salad plate but rather a shallow and generous-sized salad bowl to fill.

All entrees include soup and the salad bar. Regular offerings include a hot roast beef sandwich, deep fried catfish (all you can eat) with hush puppies and french fries, and other sandwiches and burgers served in attractive pots. The onion rings are made from an original batter and are delicious.

The dinner menu adds steaks, barbecued ribs, a huge seafood platter, Cornish game hen, and lobster tail. On special nights, you can have all you can eat for a single price. Monday nights it is barbecued beef, chicken and sausage with beans, corn on the cob, and the salad bar. Thursday nights feature fried chicken with gravy, mashed potatoes, and the salad bar. From 11 a.m. until 7 p.m. on Sundays, a buffet is also an all-you-can-eat menu. The restaurant is closed on Tuesdays and Wednesdays.

The restaurant is spread out through three of Krum's oldest "downtown" buildings. You may want to purchase a keepsake from the locally-made gift items available at the cash register counter. The many attractive items will be a pleasant reminder of the little town which may not be big but which diners from miles around have found, all because of The Clay Pot Eatery.

Serving hours: 11 a.m.–8:30 p.m. Monday and Thursday; 11 a.m.–9 p.m. Friday; 5 p.m.–9 p.m. Saturday; 11 a.m.–7 p.m. Sunday.
Closed: Tuesdays and Wednesdays, first two weeks in January, Christmas Eve and Christmas Day.
Lunch and dinner.
Cost of average meal: Lunch—inexpensive; dinner—moderate to (a few) expensive.
No credit cards accepted. Personal checks accepted.
Special occasion services: Complimentary birthday or anniversary cake.
Wheelchair accommodations: Front door.
Parking: Spacious.
No alcohol served.

"Since 1947" the sign out front reads, and the Metzler brothers have spent all those years serving up the barbecue for which they have become well known. Their restaurant is big, not fancy (no place mats nor even plates for your sandwich), but the no-frills setting is appropriate for some of the best barbecue you will ever taste.

The sliced beef is tender. Locals praise their ribs. Metzlers' takeout food can be ready in only a few minutes. A favorite local drink is a "red pitcher" of beer, which is beer laced with tomato juice. You'll find lots of diners from this area of North Texas. If a TV turned on while you eat bothers you, you can sit at the far end of the big dining room. There, a ceiling fan and softer lighting also add to a quieter atmosphere.

Metzler Brothers Barbecue

U.S. Hwy. 82, west of town
Lindsay
(214) 665-9040
Owners: Gerald, Lee, and Bill Metzler

Casual atmosphere and barbecue to go are two attractions at the Metzler family-operated restaurant.

Lee Metzler says the brothers operate on a two out of three vote among them on matters involving the restaurant. Other members of the family help out in the kitchen and out front. Each brother has a son who is in the process of learning the business and deciding if he wants to be a part of it. If the younger Metzlers do carry on the tradition of the restaurant, they will enjoy a family pride of almost forty years.

The little town of Lindsay is just across the highway, and you may want to visit their beautiful St. Peter's church, built in 1902.

Serving hours: 9:30 a.m.–12 a.m. Tuesday through Friday; 9:30 a.m.–1 a.m. Saturdays; 12 p.m.–12 a.m. Sundays.
Closed: Mondays, New Year's Day, Easter, Thanksgiving, Christmas Day.
Lunch and dinner.
Cost of average meal: Inexpensive.
No credit cards accepted. Personal checks accepted.
Wheelchair accommodations: Front door and restrooms.
Parking: Spacious.

Simple, good food is the main attraction at Rohmer's. Any day of the week except Sunday when they are closed, you'll find the little restaurant filled with local farmers, oil operators, and oilfield workers, Muenster residents, and travelers who have heard about its consistent fine food and service. Emil Rohmer has owned the restaurant since 1953. He knows his customers, and he knows what they want.

Steaks, fried chicken, barbecue, chicken fried steak, Mexican food, and fish are daily selections on the menu. Mrs. Rohmer's cheesecake is worthy of the fame it enjoys. You can choose from chocolate amaretto, pecan praline, or New York style.

The restaurant is located in a fifty-year-old stone house, much like many of the residences built in the middle 1930s. The only time you may have trouble getting a table would be during the big event in Muenster, the annual spring Germanfest.

During the last weekend in April, the small town draws thousands of visitors to participate in the Fun Run, Ladies' Smile Contest, Men's Krazy Legs Contest, Motorcycle Road-eo, and other activities, and to dance the polka, enjoy mugs of cold beer, and consume miles of German sausage, apple strudel, cheese, and homemade pastries. At this time, the Rohmers operate a booth where they serve sausage, sauerkraut, and hot German potato salad.

But during Germanfest or on any day they're open, you can count on a pleasant, filling meal at Rohmer's.

Serving hours: 7 a.m.–10 p.m. Monday through Thursday; 7 a.m.–11
   p.m. Friday and Saturday.
Closed: Sundays, New Year's Day, Easter, Memorial Day, July Fourth,
   Labor Day, Thanksgiving, Christmas Eve after 2 p.m., Christmas Day.
Breakfast, lunch, and dinner.
Cost of average meal: Inexpensive to moderate.
No credit cards accepted. Personal checks accepted.
Wheelchair accommodations: Front door.
Parking: Spacious.

Rohmer's

U.S. Hwy. 82
Muenster (west of Gainesville)
(817) 759-2973
Owner: Emil Rohmer

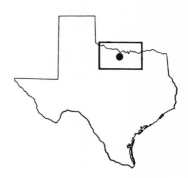

Rohmer's is located in a 1930s converted home in Muenster, west of Gainesville.

Durham House

603 N. Rogers, near Marvin
Waxahachie
(817) 937-8082
Owners: Bob Welch and Jerry
*   Weber*

Reservations and prompt arrival are required to eat at this superb destination restaurant, forty-two miles south of Fort Worth and thirty-five miles south of Dallas. The drive from either city is easy on Interstate 35, but if you are traveling and hadn't planned to pass through Waxahachie, replan your route. You won't regret it.

Durham House is only one of the dozens of beautiful, turn-of-the-century homes which have been restored in Waxahachie. (More historic buildings here are on the National Register of Historic Places than in any other Texas town the size of Waxahachie.) Durham House guests sit in four rooms, surrounded by mahogany mantels over coal-burning fireplaces, German lead crystal windows, antique chandeliers, and a crystal, brass, and pewter aquarium from Queen Victoria's day.

Meticulous attention to details both in setting and in food includes lighting which is so subtle and soft, you won't be surprised to learn it is controlled hourly by a rheostat. (Even the Christmas tree lights fade to a soft glow as the evening grows dark.) Tables are covered with pale apricot-colored cloths, and you wouldn't believe it if you were told how particular owner Bob Welch is about the placement of the table settings. Gentle music plays in the background. No pipes or cigars are allowed. Service is as smooth and fast as quicksilver. No guests under six years are permitted.

Co-owner Jerry Weber does all of the cooking. Your fresh spinach salad and peanut bisque are appropriate preludes to your choice of ten entrees. A rack of lamb is grilled medium only and served in rosemary butter with mint sauce on the side. You may prefer "Seafood Chesapeake," chunks of Alaska King Crab and large shrimp in a delicate white wine sauce served in a continually heating chafing dish. Jerry has cooked since he was eight years old and is a multi-talented man, but nowhere does his culinary talent shine better than in his "Beef Regency," a two-inch, prime, center cut sirloin, broiled rare and baked in a sauce of dry sack sherry, fresh mushrooms, artichoke hearts, shallots, butter, garlic, and cream.

Don't get the idea this is a formal, stuffy place. Not so. Before the dessert listings, the menu urges diners not to get hysterical if the waiter is unable to fill their order, because the restaurant sometimes runs out of certain desserts, since they are made on the premises and demand can't be predicted. Anyone who has his heart set on peaches melba made with French vanilla ice cream, Chambord raspberry sauce, and whipped cream may have to settle for "The Wellesley Special," praline pecan ice cream on chocolate sponge cake, topped with kahlua and chocolate sauce, whipped cream, and pecans. Sorry.

No liquor is served, but you may bring your own. There is a moderate corkage charge. If you wish, you may come a little earlier than your reservation for dinner and enjoy your drinks at your table.

Guests come from all over the United States and from foreign countries to eat at the Durham House. Movies have been made in Waxahachie in recent years, so film personalities are frequent guests. Word of mouth is the only means of advertising the restaurant relies on, and apparently it is enough. After one dinner here, you could easily find yourself spreading the good word.

Serving hours: From 6 p.m. Thursday and Fridays; from 5 p.m. Saturdays and Sundays.
Closed: Monday through Wednesday, Thanksgiving, Christmas Eve, Christmas Day.
Dinner only.
Cost of average meal: Expensive.
No credit cards accepted. Personal checks accepted.
Special occasion services: Candle on dessert.
Wheelchair accommodations: Front door and restrooms.
Reservations required.
Parking: Spacious.

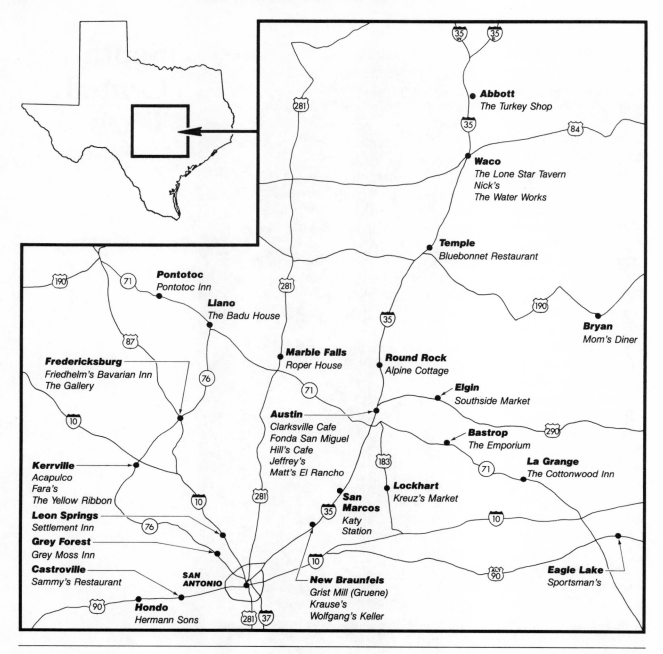

Abbott
The Turkey Shop

Waco
The Lone Star Tavern
Nick's
The Water Works

Temple
Bluebonnet Restaurant

Bryan
Mom's Diner

Pontotoc
Pontotoc Inn

Llano
The Badu House

Fredericksburg
Friedhelm's Bavarian Inn
The Gallery

Marble Falls
Roper House

Round Rock
Alpine Cottage

Elgin
Southside Market

Austin
Clarksville Cafe
Fonda San Miguel
Hill's Cafe
Jeffrey's
Matt's El Rancho

Bastrop
The Emporium

La Grange
The Cottonwood Inn

Kerrville
Acapulco
Fara's
The Yellow Ribbon

Lockhart
Kreuz's Market

Leon Springs
Settlement Inn

Grey Forest
Grey Moss Inn

San Marcos
Katy Station

Castroville
Sammy's Restaurant

Eagle Lake
Sportsman's

SAN ANTONIO

New Braunfels
Grist Mill (Gruene)
Krause's
Wolfgang's Keller

Hondo
Hermann Sons

Between Waco and Hillsboro, the little town of Abbott makes two current claims to fame: it is the home of Willie Nelson and of the Turkey Shop and Cafeteria. If you're a hungry traveler, you'll definitely want to check out the cafeteria and perhaps buy a Willie Nelson T-shirt in town.

Mrs. Tufts explains that the family operation began when Interstate 35 was being built, and she was selling only whole, dressed turkeys at her nearby ranch. Highway workers started asking her for turkey sandwiches, which she provided, and the rest is roadfood history. For twenty years motorists and area residents have been driving off I-35 to the big roadside restaurant for hickory-smoked turkey, ham, beef, and sausage.

This region of Texas was settled by hard-working Czech farmers. Their descendants still produce some of their special food. The Tufts buy their sausage from Nemecek's Market in nearby West. A local woman makes the kolaches, a fruit-filled Czech pastry for sale both in the cafeteria and in the shop in front.

The cafeteria menu is large, and everything is priced separately. The mouth-watering, smoked meat is available in both sandwiches and sliced on plates. You can select from an array of cooked vegetables, including corn, peas, lima beans, black-eyed peas, carrots, broccoli, squash, creamed potatoes, fried okra, turnip greens, and green beans. There are a variety of salads including potato, barbecued bean, pea, three-bean, slaw, and turkey. Cornbread dressing is priced as a salad. Homemade rolls and cornbread are hot and tasty. Desserts include banana pudding, cheesecake, and a hot blueberry cobbler, all made by Mrs. Tufts and her long-time assistants in the kitchen. An assortment of locally-made desserts are also served. You can even have fish or fried chicken, if you prefer. It's all so good you'll think you've gone to Grandmother's for Sunday dinner.

In the shop out front you can buy whole or half smoked turkey or ham, fresh meat, and cheese to go, and fresh baked bread from the famous Collin Street Bakery in Corsicana.

The Turkey Shop & Cafeteria

off I-35 at Abbott Exit
22 miles north of Waco
Abbott
(817) 582-2015
Owners: Gilbert Tufts and
*   sons, Mrs. Gilbert Tufts, Bob*
*   Tufts, Bryan Tufts*

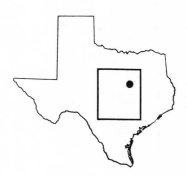

Serving hours: 8 a.m.–8 p.m. seven days a week.
Closed: Christmas Day.
Lunch, dinner, and afternoon snacks.
Cost of average meal: Inexpensive.
Most credit cards accepted. Personal checks accepted.
Wheelchair accommodations: Front door and restrooms.
Parking: Spacious.
No alcohol served.

Clarksville Cafe

1202 W. Lynn, near W. 12th,
next door to Jeffrey's
Austin
(512) 472-7279
Owners: Jeffrey Weinberger,
Ron and Peggy Weiss

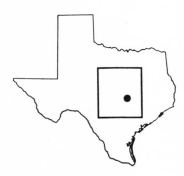

You almost have to compare Jeffrey's Restaurant next door and the Clarksville Cafe because they have the same owners. What else they share is a location in one of Austin's oldest neighborhoods, flawlessly prepared food, superb service, and decor with thoughtful attention to detail. The Clarksville is a bit more relaxed in both atmosphere and price of meals. Otherwise, it would be hard to choose between the two. (See Jeffrey's, p. 111.)

Dinner is the only meal served, and you will dine among palms, ivy, ficus, and fresh flowers. Menu choices vary from day to day, but everything is good and prepared by a chef (at this writing a woman) who is obviously trained in gourmet cooking. You can select from such salads as Linguine Marin or cold pasta salad. On your visit, entrees may include grilled redfish, layered cheese or chicken terrine, green enchiladas, a fruit and cheese plate, and hacked chicken. The latter is a rich mound of chopped chicken covered with a spicy sauce of sesame oil and seed, peanut butter, cayenne, and fresh garlic. You'll be given chopsticks to use if you wish. The homemade whole wheat bread with sesame seed is a marvelous accompaniment to any entree you choose.

For dessert the same wonderful selections as those served at Jeffrey's are offered, including "Chocolate Intemperance," "Lemon Almond Custard Torte," and a cheesecake you have to taste to believe.

One of the Clarksville's specialties is high quality drinks prepared by owner Jeff Weinberger. He uses fresh-squeezed lime juice, and you can count on being pleased. His personal involvment in the operation of the restaurant is one of the many reasons for its popularity and success.

Serving hours: 5:30 p.m.–10:30 p.m. Monday through Thursday; 5:30 p.m.–11 p.m. Friday and Saturday.
Closed: Sundays, New Year's Day, Easter, Memorial Day, July Fourth, Labor Day, Thanksgiving, Christmas Eve, Christmas Day.
Dinner only.

The Clarksville Cafe is located in one of Austin's oldest neighborhoods and features superior food in a gardenlike setting.

Cost of average meal: Moderate to expensive.
Credit cards accepted: Visa, MasterCard. No personal checks accepted.
Special occasion services: Candle in a cake.
Wheelchair accommodations: Front door and restrooms.
Parking: Spacious.

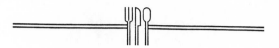

Fonda San Miguel

2430 West North Loop at
*   Hancock*
Austin
(512) 459-3401
Owners: Tom Gilliland and
*   Mike Ravago*

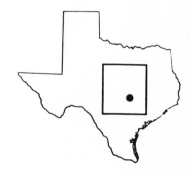

For a beautiful setting, Fonda San Miguel is matchless among the Mexican restaurants in Austin. This is the place to bring a special friend or to celebrate an important occasion. Before your meal, you may want to have a drink in the lush greenness of the semi-covered patio. In the main dining room, soft light filters through huge, pierced-tin hanging lanterns. The pink stucco walls are filled with the work of some of Mexico's finest artists, and the masks and artifacts throughout the restaurant are one of a kind.

Tall, hand-carved doors fold between the dining areas. In the bar a pretty girl stands behind the Mexican tile counter and continually heats and fills serving baskets with thin flour tortillas.

At your table you will sit in comfortable leather and wood chairs of Mexican design. The tostadas are crisp and fresh but a word of warning about the table salsa. By anyone's definition, it's hot. The menu lists several salsa variations, one of them called "mild." You may want to ask owner Tom Gilliland or Mike Ravago just "how mild"— they'll be honest, you can be sure.

You can count on a pleasant, efficient waitperson (Fonda San Miguel's preferred name), aided by a computer near the kitchen which both speeds up your order and provides a nice, legible bill at the end of your meal. This is one place where an icy glass of water is placed in front of you as soon as you sit down and is never allowed to be empty for long. Waiters with watchful eyes and water pitchers move about constantly to make sure.

If you want to learn a little Spanish or to refresh your knowledge, the menu will help. All of the selections listed in Spanish are translated underneath. Among the *antojitos* (appetizers) are *quesadillas*, flour or corn tortillas filled with white cheese and chile poblano strips. Fonda San Miguel prepares those favorite Tex-Mex munchies, *nachos*, with black beans, white cheese and Mexican sausage on top. Several tasty Mexican soups are available, but unless you are very hungry, save plenty of room for your entree.

If you aren't already an aficionado of Mexican food, don't let anyone tell you that it all tastes alike. Here you have five choices of enchilada dishes, each one distinctive and all delicious; each is served with beautifully-seasoned Mexican rice and black beans, prepared Mexican style. Then there are fish and chicken selections such as "Pescado Veracruzano," which is broiled fillet of fish in a sauce of tomatoes, onions, green olives, and capers. "Pollo Pibil" is chicken baked in banana leaves and seasoned Yucatan style with achiote, tomatoes, and onions. If red meat is your standard preference, try the "Carne Asada Tampiqueña," a marinated and charbroiled strip of heart of beef tenderloin, served with poblano chile strips and onions, guacamole, black beans, and your choice of green, red, or Mole cheese enchiladas and flour tortillas.

For dessert (dessert!), how about mangoes and ice cream with the mangoes cooked with tequila and triple sec? A chocolate and Kahlua pie? Flan?

Serving hours: 11 a.m.–2 p.m. weekdays; 11:30 a.m.–2 p.m. Sunday brunch; 5:30 p.m.–10 p.m. weekdays; 5:30 p.m.–11 p.m. Fridays and Saturdays.
Closed: Thanksgiving and Christmas Day.
Sunday brunch, lunch, dinner.
Cost of average meal: Moderate.
Credit cards accepted: Visa, MasterCard, Diners Card, Carte Blanche. No personal checks accepted.
Special occasion services: 24 hours' notice for special cakes.
Wheelchair accommodations: Front door and restrooms.
Parking: Spacious.

Hill's Cafe

4700 S. Congress
Austin
(512) 442-1471
Owners: "Boomer" Goodnight
and John Harris

It would be only a little bit of exaggeration to say that Hill's Cafe can trace its history all the way back to Colonel Goodnight of trailblazing and Panhandle ranching fame—but only a little bit. The cafe has been run, in part, by the Goodnight family of Austin for over thirty-five years, and its western atmosphere and rustic decor reflect its heritage.

"Boomer" Goodnight is the son of Charlie Goodnight who earned countless restaurant association awards and honors for the restaurant which began in 1947 as a twenty-four-hour-a-day coffee shop. The present-day coffee shop and restaurant are still open twenty-four

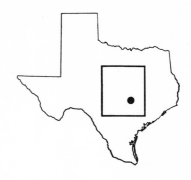

hours a day, serving sizzling steaks and chicken fried steaks along with wonderful hot rolls and Texas-sized glasses of iced tea.

A tremendous personal pride in the business shines in his face when "Boomer" talks about how they gathered the native field stone and cedar for the restaurant's expansion. He likes to show guests the attractive murals done by artist Frank Brewer, which show the Goodnight party in Palo Duro Canyon and a Barton Springs scene in Austin. He points out that some of his employees have twenty to thirty years' tenure with the restaurant. (The butcher started at the age of eighteen.) And he'll speak with regret about the gradual disappearance of many home-owned restaurants in the state and elsewhere.

Order a sizzling steak or one which is chicken fried. Your baked potato will be one of the biggest and best you've ever tasted. All the salad dressings are homemade. Everything is first-rate. You can order breakfast, lunch or dinner and also snacks twenty-four hours a day.

Originally called the San Antonio Road, South Congress Street leads straight from the state capitol through downtown Austin to connect south of town with Interstate Highway 35. Not many wagons nor stagecoaches travel that route these days, but when you stop, you'll find the spacious parking lot filled with every modern kind of vehicle there is. Once you've eaten at Hill's Cafe, you'll understand its popularity and many years of success.

Serving hours: Twenty-four hours a day.
Closed: Thanksgiving, Christmas Day.
Breakfast, lunch, and dinner.
Cost of average meal: Moderate.
Credit cards accepted: Visa, MasterCard. No personal checks accepted.
Wheelchair accommodations: Front door and restrooms.
Parking: Spacious.

If top quality food, attentive service, and attractive but simple decor are all equally important to you—and the cost really doesn't matter—then Jeffrey's will more than meet your expectations. The menu always contains beatifully prepared continental selections. The service is superb. And the surroundings suggest casual elegance. Only the prices alongside the menu listings written on the wall blackboard are not so casual. But if you don't mind about the cost, then sit back and enjoy it all from the attentive waiters to the fresh rose on each table. You'll be surrounded by well-dressed Austin diners who know to come early for immediate seating.

First, you may want to try one of the rich soups, such as tomato with succulent fish chunks, made with tomato and duck stocks and seasoned delicately with saffron and fennel. Typical of the entrees are roast duck, redfish, lamb, ribeye steak, softshell crabs, and sweetbreads, all flawlessly prepared. They call one dessert "Chocolate Intemperance," and it will drive all thoughts of dieting into next Thursday.

Jeffrey's

1204 W. Lynn, near W. 12th,
*   next door to Clarksville Cafe*
Austin
(512) 477-5584
Owners: Ron and Peggy Weiss,
*   Jeff Weinberger*

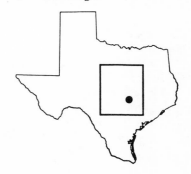

A good wine list is in keeping with the overall excellence of Jeffrey's.

Most of the parking is across the street in business parking lots, unused during the evening hours.

Serving hours: 6:30–11 p.m. Monday–Saturday.
Closed: Sundays, New Year's Day, July Fourth, Labor Day,
    Thanksgiving, Christmas Day, New Year's Eve.
Dinner only.
Cost of average meal: Expensive.
Credit cards accepted: Visa, MasterCard. Personal checks accepted.
Special occasion services: Candle on dessert.
Wheelchair accommodations: Front door, restrooms.
Parking: Spacious, across the street.
Wine only.

Matt's El Rancho

303 E. First at Congress
Austin
(512) 472-5425
Owners: Matt and Janie
*   Martinez, Matt Martinez, Jr.*

"See the difference pride makes." That should be the slogan of Matt's El Rancho. Instead, soft-spoken Matt Martinez calls himself the "King of Mexican Food," and that's all right, too. Either way, if you ever find yourself in the capital city with time to eat at only one Mexican restaurant, this is the one.

Matt, Sr., as he is most often called, and wife Janie reign over the largest Mexican restaurant in Austin, and they show justifiable pride in their thirty-plus year operation. They must sometimes look across busy First Street at the location of the little house which served as the restaurant where Janie worked as a cook and Matt as a waiter many

Matt Martinez's El Rancho is Austin's largest Mexican food restaurant but provides intimate seating along with consistently good food.

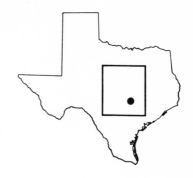

years ago. From such humble beginnings, they have built one of the most popular restaurants in Austin, where photos of well-known guests line the walls. Alongside the photos hang framed awards, including both the 1982 and 1983 Silver Spoon Award, presented by the Gourmet Diner Club of America.

El Rancho serves over a thousand people a day. All the recipes are those developed by the Martinezes who guarantee every item is made fresh daily. In addition to the restaurant, they own the tortilla factory on the corner, which provides some of the ingredients for such dishes as their chicken flautas (a tightly rolled tortilla filled with chicken and topped with sour cream, white cheese and chile con queso) and green enchiladas filled with chicken or beef and topped with sour cream or chile con queso. They also prepare Mexican seafood dishes, including "Shrimp a la Matt Martinez," served with cheese and bean flautas and guacamole salad. Another taste-pleaser is the chile relleno with chicken. The plate is a feast for the eye as well, with melted cheese covering the chile, topped with sour cream lightly sprinkled with pecans and raisins. Beware of the chile hiding innocently underneath. By any taste standard, it's hot.

If you've never tasted sopaipillas, or even if you have, try the Martinez version. You get four to an order, and there's no better way to end a Mexican meal at El Rancho than with an airy sopaipilla filled with honey.

Wine, beer, and mixed drinks are available, and Matt has a special sangria drink he calls "Matt's Magic Sangria." All he'll say about it is that it has some peach brandy in it, and "One of these and you think you're a magician!"

Serving hours: 11 a.m.–10 p.m. every day except Tuesday.
Closed: Tuesdays, New Year's Day, Easter, Labor Day, Thanksgiving, Christmas Day.
Breakfast, lunch, and dinner.
Cost of average meal: Inexpensive to moderate.
Credit cards accepted: American Express, Visa, MasterCard, Carte Blanche. No personal checks accepted.
Special occasion services: Sopaipillas.
Wheelchair accommodations: Front door.
Special required dress: Shoes and shirt at all times.
Reservations: Only needed for ten or more persons.
Parking: Spacious.

The Emporium

In Bastrop's Emporium, memories are as thick as its walls of river clay brick and stucco. Part of the building was used as a customs house during the 1830s and may have been the place where Stephen F. Austin paid his tithe in gold to his Mexican landlords before establishing one of the state's first settlements. Now Peggy Burrows and Ann Emmert have combined their talents to make the neat building open again to the public and add to the number of almost 160 registered historical places in the town.

813 Main, exit on Loop 150 off State Hwy. 71
Bastrop
(512) 321-4198
Owners: Peggy Burrows and Ann Emmert

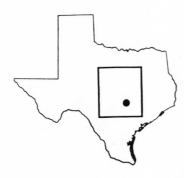

Peggy's expertise is antiques, and one portion of The Emporium serves as an antique shop where visitors may browse among the warm glow of European antiques before or after lunch. Ann contributes her gift of creating slow-cooked soups, tasty, overstuffed sandwiches, home-baked breads, salads, sour cream apple pie, and cheesecake. One of her cakes, the "1886 Chocolate Cake," is a recipe from the Driskill Hotel's 1886 Tea Room Cook Book. Lunch is the only meal served, but soft drinks or coffee and tea and desserts are available all day.

You may eat in the front room which once served as a bakery and also as a tavern. The patchwork of the Mexican tile floor was discovered during restoration, and it has some tiles with bluebonnets, others with cactus design. Saltillo tiles cover the pecan-shaded patio to the side of the building where you can enjoy your lunch and listen to the falling water sounds of the fountain.

Serving hours: 11 a.m.–2:30 p.m. Tuesday through Saturday.
Closed: Sundays, Mondays, New Year's Day, July Fourth, Thanksgiving, Christmas Day.
Lunch and afternoon snacks.
Cost of average meal: Inexpensive.
Special occasion services: Dessert with a candle and song.
No credit cards accepted. Personal checks accepted.
Wheelchair accommodations: Front door and restrooms.
Parking: Spacious.
No alcohol served.

Mom's Diner

1207 E. 25th off State Hwy. 6
Bryan
(409) 779-8600
Owner: Don Mahan

Add to your guidelines for finding a good restaurant: If it's half hidden down a little, tree-shaded, residential street, if it's located in an old house or nondescript building, if most people you ask about it doubt that you'll be able to find it but are more than willing to show you, and if you aren't sure you've found it but parked outside what *might* be the place are cars and pickups belonging to the sheriff, the gas company, and various individuals, then you've found it.

Look for the sign out front on a tree-lined, residential street where Aggies and locals have enjoyed home cooking for over fifty years.

In Bryan, it was known as Mom's Boarding House to thousands of hungry Aggies for over fifty years, and "Mom" was Mrs. R. E. Carlton. Now it is simply Mom's Diner, owned and run in much the same way by Don Mahan. If good food is more important to you than your surroundings, then Mom's is your kind of place.

You'll sit at tables for six, eat from plastic dishes, drink pre-sweetened iced tea from a quart Mason jar, and select your menu from a weekly lineup of a different entree each day, served family style from big bowls on the table. You can be sure the food will make the simple decor totally irrelevant. Mondays there is chicken fried steak and meat loaf, Tuesdays fried chicken and meat loaf, Wednesdays enchiladas, Thursdays chicken fried steak and meat loaf, Fridays catfish and meat loaf, and Saturdays enchiladas. In addition, each day the tables are loaded with assorted fresh vegetables, homemade bread, and desserts. One modest price for all you can eat.

Remember now, in Bryan it's the little house, down a narrowish residential street, with the big magnolia tree and a sign out front. You can't miss it. Just look for the cars—and the satisfied looks on the faces of the people coming out.

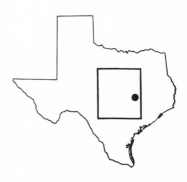

Serving hours: 11 a.m.–1:30 p.m., 5 p.m.–8 p.m. Monday through Saturday.
Closed: Sundays, New Year's Day, Christmas Day.
Lunch and dinner.
Cost of average meal: Inexpensive.
No credit cards accepted. Personal checks accepted.
Special occasion services: Cakes for parties with reservations.
Wheelchair accommodations: Front door.
Parking: Spacious.
No alcohol served.

Sammy's Restaurant

U.S. Hwy. 90 E.
Castroville
(512) 538-2204
Owners: Samuel H. and
Yvonne H. Tschirhart

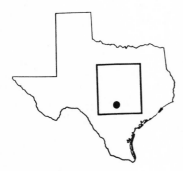

One guidebook to the little town of Castroville, east of San Antonio, lists one hundred and thirty-nine historic structures, some of which house the more than a dozen antique and gift shops. History is still visible in "The Little Alsace of Texas." Most of today's residents are descendants of the settlers from the Rhine Valley who were brought to Texas in 1844. They named their village after the man who brought them, Henri Castro of France.

Food in Castroville is characterized by the mixture of cultures represented there today. At Christmas, hot tamales as well as anise cookies are eaten, and good luck in the new year is insured by Alsatian New Year bread as well as by blackeyed peas. At Sammy's Restaurant, you can sample some of it all. Mostly, however, its fame is based on serving the best in home-style cooking and on generous portions.

Red beans and homemade noodles are favorites, and these often accompany the entrees. One of the popular choices is steak smothered with gravy, cheese, and onions. Chicken fried steak also reigns here. And the Tschirharts say they serve a lot of Mexican food as well as fried fish platters.

Before you have another onion roll with your meal, think ahead to dessert. They make a banana split pie which can only be seen and eaten to be appreciated. Mere words are useless. Imagine a combination of chocolate cream, vanilla cream, and bananas over a chocolate crust, easily four inches thick. After having a meal including some or all of the above, you won't wonder about the contented looks on the faces of the local men sitting at the big, house table. They gather for coffee each morning, and many return for lunch. Sam and Yvonne Tschirhart know them all by name, and they extend their easy, warm hospitality to strangers as well.

Across the street is their Haby's Alsatian Bakery, which you may be understandably tempted to visit, but sweet rolls and bread baked there are for sale at the front of the restaurant.

In Castroville you probably won't hear anyone say, "Y'all come back, now." But you know they want you to, and as you leave Sammy's, you'll promise yourself to return.

Serving hours: 6 a.m.–11 p.m. Sunday through Thursday; 6 a.m.–11:30
    p.m. Friday and Saturday.
Closed: Christmas Day only.
Breakfast, lunch, and dinner.
Cost of average meal: Inexpensive.
No credit cards accepted. No personal checks accepted.
Special occasion services: Birthday cake.
Wheelchair accommodations: Front door.
Parking: Spacious.

Eagle Lake, southwest of Houston, is in rice-growing country and bills itself as the "Goose Capital of the World." Rice farmers sit at one big table for breakfast each morning, and during goose season, hunters stop off for a hearty breakfast or lunch. At dinner time, Eagle Lake residents and travelers make up most of the crowd.

Doug and Janie Schwemm proudly tell guests that their food is the freshest and best they can buy and prepare. Their noon buffet is popular for its variety and is offered Sunday through Friday. Among their most popular dishes are a one-pound T-bone steak, a two-pound flounder, catfish, shrimp, and possibly the best chicken-fried steak you will have anywhere in the state. The crust is thick, the gravy is thick, and the meat is tender—an unbeatable combination. Two of their specialties are ice cream drinks and cheesecake, made fresh daily and which are available for dessert or for an afternoon snack.

If you're driving west from Houston on I-10, Eagle Lake is just a short drive south of Columbus. Children in your party will enjoy looking at the mounted bobcat and mixed-breed goose in the Sportman's entrance.

Doug's restaurant experience includes his position as food and beverage director for Marriott hotels. Janie is an Eagle Lake native. Together, they will make you feel welcome and special, demonstrating the attitude toward their guests which all good restaurant owners know means success.

Serving hours: 5:30 a.m.–9 p.m. Monday through Friday; 5:30 a.m.–1 p.m. Sundays.
Closed: New Year's Day, Memorial Day, July Fourth, Labor Day, Thanksgiving, Christmas Day.
Breakfast, lunch, and dinner.
Cost of average meal: Breakfast, lunch—inexpensive; dinner—inexpensive to moderate.
Special plates and menu selections for children, dieters and senior citizens upon request.
Credit cards accepted: Visa, MasterCard. Personal checks with proper identification accepted.
Special occasion services: Complimentary dessert for birthdays and anniversaries.
Wheelchair accommodations: Front door and restrooms.
Parking: Spacious.

Sportman's Restaurant

201 Boothe Drive, Eagle Lake
Exit off I-10
Eagle Lake
(409) 234-3071
Owners: Doug and Janie
Schwemm

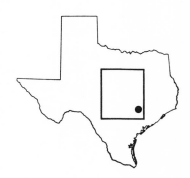

When you eat in a place you're told "was 101 years old on Sunday," and people are still pouring into the plain, no-frills rooms as you are leaving, you really don't need to ask many questions of the owners about the reasons behind its success. The Southside Market in Elgin speaks for itself.

Located by the railroad tracks and not looking anything at all like a restaurant, the Southside Market has a meat market in the front. Through the door and onto the lightly-sprinkled-with-sawdust floors, you know instantly why you came. The fragrances of smoked sausage, brisket, and beef steak fill the light, airy dining rooms. At

Southside Market

109 Central, Loop 109 off U.S.
Hwy. 290
Elgin
(512) 285-3883
Owners: Ernest W. and Adrene
Bracewell, Ernest W. Jr. and
Jeanne Bracewell

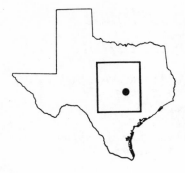

the back you can buy meat by the pound or barbecued brisket on a bun, then pick up pickles, onion slices, and jalapeños along with bread slices by the cash register. Your plate is the white paper your meat is wrapped in. There is a big selection of soft drinks but no beer, beans, potato salad, or other common barbecue companions, but you won't care. The sausage is hot but "not too hot" (that favorite, innocent phrase of Texas waitresses), and if you want it hotter there is hot sauce in tall tequila bottles on each table.

Customers are nice-looking, elderly ladies; shirt-and-tie-clad young businessmen; casually-dressed travelers; and lots of obvious regulars who drop in from work at noontime.

If you wish, you can go across the street to the pretty little park and eat on one of the stone benches. The park received the Governor's Community Achievement Award for beautifying the town, and you'll agree it deserved the honor.

The market makes around 10,000 pounds of sausage each week and supplies numerous Austin barbecue pits and several grocery stores. But it's more fun to eat off of white butcher paper and splash hot sauce from a tequila bottle on your meat at a table inside the market in Elgin.

Serving hours: 7 a.m.–6 p.m. Monday through Saturday.
Closed: Sundays, New Year's Day, July Fourth, Labor Day,
    Thanksgiving, Christmas Day.
Breakfast, lunch, and dinner.
Cost of average meal: Inexpensive.
No credit cards accepted. Personal checks accepted with identification.
Wheelchair accommodations: Front door.
Special required dress: Shirt, shoes.
Parking: Limited.
No alcohol served.

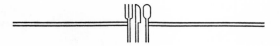

Friedhelm's Bavarian Inn

West end of Main Street
Fredericksburg
(512) 999-7024
Owner: Friedhelm C. Bopp

Fredericksburg is the perfect town for the hungry traveler to stop. Scattered along Main Street, between the old limestone buildings now used for antique stores and other businesses and shops, are numerous bakeries, deli's, and restaurants. If the main street, which is also U.S. Highways 290 and 87 and State Highway 16, were not so broad, you could follow your nose from one delicious fragrance to another.

This beautiful Old World town still reflects its German roots in many of its restaurants, and one of the best is Friedhelm's Bavarian Inn. Here you can be sure the food is authentically German, because much of it is prepared by owner and master chef Freidhelm Bopp who was born in Heidelberg. If you need further explanation of the German dishes on the menu, Bopp or his pretty wife Hilda will give

you one, with a pride in their eyes that makes you know whatever you order will be special.

Bopp describes the preparation of a one-inch thick pork chop listed on the menu as "Panierte Schweinskoteletten." He covers it with a Bavarian Swiss cheese and a tomato sauce whose ingredients you would never guess. Try it, then ask. Or you may want the "Sauerbraten, Bavarian Style," which is a *lot* of beef roast, thinly sliced and covered with a delectable sauce. All the entrees are served with riced, German-fried potatoes, and red cabbage or sauerkraut.

Everything, from the German rye bread placed on your table before you have time to order to the apple strudel you can have for dessert, is served *hot*. "And not from a microwave," Bopp makes clear. "These dishes are fresh from the oven." You can easily believe it.

Another entree with an intriguing-sounding German name (especially intriguing if you don't speak German) is "Sauerbraten Nach" or "Bayrischer Art Mit Kartoffelkoesse Und Rotkraut," which translates to Bavarian Style with Aromatic Spices, Herbs, and Wine. All the schnitzels (cutlets) are pork loin rather than the veal used by many German restaurants. Bopp feels that pork has "a heartier taste."

The dinner menu is a bit more elaborate than that for lunch, with potato dumplings offered as a side dish. If you prefer not to sample the German food (what a thought!), you have your choices of ribeye steak, catfish, fried chicken, chicken fried steak, pork chops, calves' liver, lamb chops, even sandwiches. However, two of the sandwiches will also give you a taste of the German cooking expertise in the kitchen—the sauerbraten on rye topped with sauerbraten sauce and served with German-fried potatoes, or knackwurst on rye with mustard, onions, and potatoes. A crisp chef's salad is also available.

Beverages include imported and domestic beers, house wines such as Liebfraumilch, Lambrusco, and Rose, and other German, French, and California wines. A full bar serves drinks with meals and is open every afternoon at 3:00.

Desserts can be ordered from a selection of apple strudel, Black Forest cake, chocolate mousse, and cheesecake.

The restaurant is pleasantly decorated and features a sign at the entrance which reads "Willkommen." Superb service emphasizes the message. You'll feel welcome when you arrive and glad you came when you leave.

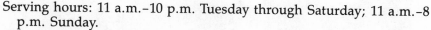

Serving hours: 11 a.m.–10 p.m. Tuesday through Saturday; 11 a.m.–8 p.m. Sunday.
Closed: Christmas Day.
Lunch and dinner, afternoon snacks.
Cost of average meal: Moderate.
Credit cards accepted: Visa, MasterCard. Local checks and other checks with proper ID accepted.
Special occasion services: Black Forest cake with candles for birthdays and anniversaries.
Wheelchair accommodations: Front door and restrooms.
Parking: Spacious.

The Gallery

230 E. Main
Fredericksburg
(512) 997-5157
Owners: Gen. James S. and
*   Francis Heard Billups*

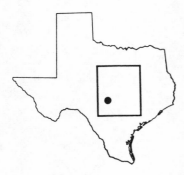

In Fredericksburg, where buildings with historical significance are as common as German names, The Gallery adds another dimension to your choices of food. Located in a 1915-vintage building which was once a restaurant, a barbershop, and a rooming house, and which still contains the handsome, original bar, this attractive restaurant is the focus of both local diners and travelers each evening Tuesday through Saturday.

What it may sometimes lack in service is more than compensated for in the quality of the food—and drinks. Manager Tom Musselman has created a drink he calls "The Texas Tumbleweed," innocently described on the menu as "vodka and cream," but he admits to a dash of tequila and kahlua. Or you may feel adventuresome enough to try a "Damn the Weather," "made with gin." A good wine list is also offered.

If you want to get right down to the pleasure of eating, appetizers include marinated artichoke hearts, French onion soup, and gazpacho. The "Classic French" house dressing for your salad would be hard to surpass. Entrees are mostly excellent steaks and seafoods or combination of both. "Flounder Napoleon" is a richly-buttered filet in a Gallery mayonnaise sauce. Other entrees include top sirloin with stuffed crab, veal Cordon Bleu, and a vegetable plate with four deliciously-steamed vegetables and a salad. The fried mushrooms are so light, you expect them to float off your plate, and the steamed celery, topped with slivered almonds, is delicately delicious.

Lighting in the restaurant is dim but adequate to see the fine examples of western art along the wall. You'll want to linger, especially on a Saturday night when the place gets livelier than you would imagine from the wide, quiet Main Street outside.

Continental dishes and drinks with names like "The Texas Tumbleweed" are served at The Gallery in Fredericksburg.

Serving hours: 5 p.m–10 p.m. Tuesday through Saturday.
Closed: Sundays, Mondays, New Year's Day, July Fourth, Thanksgiving,
    Christmas Day.
Dinner only.
Cost of average meal: Moderate to expensive.
Credit cards accepted: American Express, Visa, MasterCard, Diners
    Club, Carte Blanche. Personal checks accepted.
Special occasion services: "Within limits, any food or drink requested."
Wheelchair accommodations: Front door.
Special required dress: No cut-offs.
Reservations: Requested but not required.
Parking: Spacious.

The Grey Moss Inn

Scenic Loop Rd. off Bandera
    Rd. (State Hwy. 16), 12 miles
    from Loop 410
Grey Forest
(512) 695-8301
Owners: Jerry and Mary
    Martin

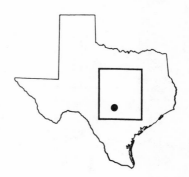

If this book were called simply "Very Special Restaurants," the Grey Moss Inn would have to be included. But even though Grey Forest is more a settlement of resort cottages and a wild life sanctuary rather than a "hometown," the restaurant deserves to be included. Steak is the primary reason most people go, but the location alone is reason enough. Be sure to start out well before dark unless you know the area. From San Antonio, take Bandera Road (only occasionally marked State Highway 16) and head north past 410. Shortly after Helotes, you will see a yellow flashing light where you turn right onto winding, tree-lined Scenic Loop. The restaurant is three miles from the turnoff, nestled in a thick oak woods.

The area is steeped in legend and history, and you can read about it on the back of the menu while you enjoy your steak or chicken. Recipes and the techniques for preparing them were developed over fifty years ago by the original owner, Mary Howell. Today steaks and chicken are charcoal-broiled to your order on the old well grill on the patio where you may choose to eat under a starry Texas sky. While you wait for your entree, you might want to try Grey Moss oysters, rolled in seasoned crumbs and sauteed in butter, an original creation by current owner Jerry Martin. Fresh asparagus with lemon herb dressing is usually available, and "Tomatoes Marie" with the same dressing always is.

A salad must be ordered separately, but with your steak or chicken you get the restaurant's famous olive twists, a tasty, rolled pastry with an olive filling. Each entree also comes with the standard vegetables—squash au gratin and sour cream baked potato, both delicious. You need to allow thirty minutes for the charcoaling of the grilled chicken, which is also basted, as are the steaks, with the Inn's original "witches brew" sauce. It is slightly sweet and smoky. All of the food is fresh. Even the water used in cooking and serving is drawn from spring wells.

The restaurant has been described as one of the most romantic in the state, and in most respects, it no doubt is. The high noise level and wide tables inside would interfere with intimate dining, but details such as fabric place mats, candlelight, and subdued colors all contribute to the atmosphere. Service is excellent, and the waiters are thoughtful and unobtrusive.

Serving hours: 5 p.m.–10 p.m. Tuesday through Sunday.
Closed: Mondays, Thanksgiving, Christmas Eve, Christmas Day.
Dinner only.
Cost of average meal: Expensive.
Credit cards accepted: American Express, Visa, MasterCard. No personal checks accepted.
Special occasion services: Candle in one of our desserts, "Happy Birthday" sung.
Wheelchair accommodations: Front door and restrooms.
Reservations requested.
Parking: Spacious.

Hermann Sons Steak House

U.S. Hwy. 90 E.
Hondo
(512) 426-2220
Owners: Leroy and Grace
*   Britsch*

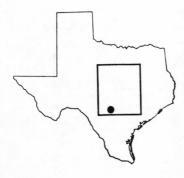

If you're just passing through this part of Texas, or if you're a native and you want to show visitors a restaurant which is as "Texas" as you can get, drop in for a meal at Hermann Sons Steak House. This place gives new meaning to the description, *country-western*. The building itself is ramshackle on the outside, off the road a bit in a shady grove of mesquite and oak trees.

Inside is the big dining room and the large room mostly used for the bar but pressed into dining space on a Sunday noon when everyone in Medina County must eat there. Dress is casual for the most part, and on an October day, some of the archery-equipped deer hunters are in camouflaged attire, raring to go. Even with a crowd, the Britsches have their staff so well trained that service is swift and efficient. The carefree dress and friendly exchanges between diners and waitresses are appropriate in the big, neon-lighted room where beer signs from practically every brewery in the country are displayed and add even more local color.

On the walls are signs reading: "A favor, Please. Everyone loves children in their place, and their place is at their table with Mother and Father." Parents seem to take the admonition seriously.

The big attraction at Hermann Sons is the steaks, in particular their hamburger steak, laced with chopped onions and Serranos chiles. You can order yours large or regular, hot, medium-hot, or mild. They'll add cheese if you like or top the piquant concoction with chili. Then, naturally, you can have, instead, chicken fried steak or almost any cut of broiled steak.

Their small order of onion rings is a small *platter* of onion rings, easily enough for two people. They are lightly battered, golden halos, understandably popular with Hermann Sons' regular diners.

The menu includes all the usual, home-type, Texas dishes with the exception of barbecue. A senior citizen's dinner offers beef, fish, or chicken with a choice of salad bar or soup, baked potato or french fries, and tea or coffee, all for a very reasonable price. Children under twelve years may choose from fried chicken, fried fish, chopped sirloin, steak fingers, a single taco, or an enchilada. The restaurant will prepare any item to go.

Either before or after your meal, you would enjoy a peek inside the big old yellow Southern Pacific Railroad depot across the road. Built about 1897, today it is a marvelous museum with dozens of items depicting the country's development. Youngsters can tap a real telegraph key or sit in an old-fashioned schoolroom.

Serving hours: 11 a.m.–9:30 p.m. Tuesday through Sunday.
Closed: Mondays, Easter, Thanksgiving, Christmas Eve, Christmas Day.
Lunch and dinner.
Cost of average meal: Inexpensive to moderate.
Credit cards accepted: Visa, MasterCard. Personal checks accepted.
Special occasion services: Cakes for birthdays and a song.
Wheelchair accommodations: Front door and restrooms.
Parking: Spacious.

Naturally, if you're just passing through a town, you can't know that the owners and many of the employees at the restaurant you choose all have the same last name. Nor can you know when you arrive that the mayor of the town, the chamber of commerce head, and various other city officials are eating there as they do regularly. But if you could know these things, you would know you've chosen a winner.

The Hernandez family of the Acapulco Restaurant have combined their energies to serve up such popular dishes as tacos al carbon, enchiladas, chalupas, compuestas, and superior margaritas. Rocky

Acapulco Restaurant

1550 Junction Highway
Kerrville
(512) 896-2232
Owners: Joe and Rocky
*   Hernandez*

Hernandez will describe the preparation of tacos al carbon with the same enthusiasm he must have had when he played football for the University of Houston. (Restaurant owners' backgrounds vary, and many have no relation to the restaurant business. Joe Hernandez is a CPA.) The beef is marinated for twenty-four hours in a sauce made of soy sauce, Worcestershire, lemon and lime juices, onions, cayenne, garlic powder, and a little salt and pepper. Then the beef is smoked over mesquite wood. The result is like nothing you ever tasted before. The menu is huge, and you will have a hard time deciding on an entree, but it will be fantastic, you can be sure.

The service is fast and the surroundings attractive and pleasant. Oh, yes, besides the already-mentioned prominent guests, you may dine with members of the Kerrville High School Key Club, the football team, the Homebuilders Association, the Bar Association, or the local Board of Realtors. They are regular diners, too.

Serving hours: 11 a.m.–2 p.m., 5 p.m.–9:30 p.m. Monday through
    Thursday; 5 p.m.–10 p.m. Friday and Saturday.
Closed: Sundays, New Year's Day, Labor Day. Thanksgiving, Christmas
    Eve, Christmas Day.
Lunch and dinner.
Cost of average meal: Inexpensive.
Credit cards accepted: Visa, MasterCard. No personal checks accepted.
Wheelchair accommodations: Front door.
Parking: Spacious.

Fara's International Restaurant

1201 Broadway (State Hwy. 27)
Kerrville
(512) 896-6580
Owners: Faramarz T. Farahani
*   and Fariborz Malek*

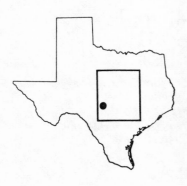

Fara's split-level, gardenlike setting is a quiet, lovely place to enjoy perfectly prepared steaks, seafood, or Italian dishes. Guests with palates sensitive to good pasta will immediately recognize Fara's as homemade. Here it is combined with a wide choice of Italian entrees, several featuring veal and eggplant.

The shrimp scampi looks as if it belongs in the color photographs of a gourmet magazine and is delicious. You can also have steak scampi, a combination of steak and shrimp or almost any cut of steak you desire.

Lovers of Greek food will be happy to discover dolmeh—stuffed grape leaves which many people consider the real food of the gods. A big "Mediterranean Salad" is another Greek specialty, containing lettuce, tomatoes, ham, cheese, olives, eggs, and peppers. A sprinkling of fresh herbs makes the house dressing on the dinner salad especially good. The garlic bread is hot and hearty, and ice in the good, strong iced tea is honest ice, not fast-melting slivers which you often find in restaurants.

Service is top quality (and not just for visiting writers). No mixed drinks but a good selection of wines and beers. Fara's is a romantic place to eat a leisurely meal and linger, surrounded by greenery indoors and outdoors.

You can enjoy homemade pasta, steaks, shrimp, or Greek food in the garden setting of Fara's.

Serving hours: 11:30 a.m.–2 p.m. Sunday through Friday; 5:30 p.m.–9:30 p.m. Monday through Saturday; 5:30 p.m.–10:30 p.m. Friday and Saturday.
Closed: Sunday nights, Thanksgiving, Christmas Day.
Lunch and dinner.
Cost of average meal: Moderate.
Credit cards accepted: American Express, Visa, MasterCard. Local personal checks accepted.
Wheelchair accommodations: Front door.
Reservations requested on weekends.
Parking: Limited.

How can you know for certain that a restaurant is going to live up to its great reputation before you eat there? One way is to drop in on a day in August and hear a local woman asking about arrangements for a Christmas luncheon. Another is to watch a cluster of guests who have obviously been there before, returning for another meal before the door opens for dinner.

You probably wouldn't want to have only one item for a meal, much less just dessert, but if extreme circumstances were to force you to make this choice, go on, order the "Lemon Alaska Pie." Ridiculous? But listen: it's a confection made of layered vanilla ice cream over a thin, creamy, lightly-flavored lemon sauce, over a pecan bits

The Yellow Ribbon

Left on Tivy off Broadway, four blocks east of courthouse
Kerrville
(512) 896-6416
Owners: C. C. and Naomi Huffhines

Once the girlhood home of Mrs. Coke Stevenson, this beautiful old Victorian house now is home to the elegant Yellow Ribbon restaurant.

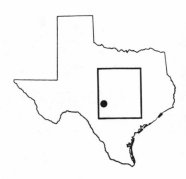

crust, wrapped in a meringue baked just long enough to give it a whisper of toasty brown. If that idea doesn't appeal to you, how about having only the jalapeño soup? Not too hot (honest), but rich and beefy, spiced with celery bits and other indefinable but luscious-tasting things.

However, if you really want an entire meal, you can have both of these and a choice of some of the most elegant, though not expensive, food you will ever have *anywhere*. With your soup you'll be served a little plate of made-fresh-daily cheese wafers you'll be telling your friends about. For lunch you might have "Chicken Breast a la Maison," a beautiful, butterflied chicken breast cooked in white wine and served over a brown and wild rice blend. Timbales hold crisp-cooked vegetables in their creamy mounds. Hot bran muffins accompany every entree.

The luncheon menu also offers "Veal Vaduz," cooked with herbs and wine, mixed with sour cream and capers, and red snapper, London Broil, ribeye steak, and Fettucine Alfredo. Among the "Lighter Fare" choices are seafood crepes with hollandaise sauce, quiche, and escargots with noodles.

For dinner you have an even wider range of selections: frog legs, shrimp scampi, flounder, trout, "Beef and Reef," which is a filet and a lobster tail, also roast duckling, and a New York sirloin pepper steak.

If you have somehow passed by the "Lemon Alaska Pie," you won't regret having black and white cheesecake, topped with chocolate and sour cream. All the desserts are made in the restaurant daily.

A wide range of beverages is available, including mixed drinks, wine, beer, and champagne.

With only twelve tables inside the beautiful old Victorian house, reservations are almost a must. After your meal, you'll want to take time to stroll through the rooms, once the girlhood home of the late Mrs. Coke Stevenson and from 1905 to 1976 that of D. H. Comparette and his family. One of the dining rooms was the music room, and through the plant-filled window you can see a huge willow tree and part of the grounds. Upstairs you'll find more antique-filled rooms, one of which offers items for sale.

C. C. and Naomi Huffhines so obviously love their work and their guests, it is little wonder The Yellow Ribbon is such a favorite restaurant for Kerrville residents and out-of-town visitors alike. If there is one flawless, home-owned restaurant in the state, this would have to be it.

Serving hours: 11 a.m.–2 p.m., 5:30 p.m.–9:30 p.m.
Closed: Tuesdays, Christmas Day.
Lunch and dinner.
Cost of average meal: Lunch—moderate; dinner—moderate to
    expensive.
Credit cards accepted: Visa, MasterCard, Diners Club, Carte Blanche.
    Personal checks accepted.
Special occasion services: Cake with candles and a song.
Wheelchair accommodations: Front door and women's restroom.
Reservations requested.
Parking: Spacious.

"Just Good Food," The Cottonwood Inn promises its guests, and for thirty-three years Jean and "Boss" Hrbacek have lived up to that promise. First serving only hot dogs, chili, and hamburgers, the Hrbaceks say the place "just grew and grew," and today it's famous for steaks that come to your table sizzling. The tenderloin strip is their specialty, but Boss assures you that even his hamburger meat is ground steak and also that no tenderizer is used on any steak.

Another popular dish is their beef-filled enchiladas with no skimping on the meat. If you want a blend of steak with Mexican flavor, try "Hallie's Special," a chopped sirloin with onions, cheese, and jalapeños. You won't go away hungry. In case you're tempted to fill up on bread before your order comes (not likely since the service is so good), remember that you can buy a loaf of the delicious homemade bread to take with you.

Friday and Saturday nights the adjoining private club has country and western live music.

Boss Hrbacek is a busy man and may be away from the restaurant, involved in one of his many other business interests, but Jean or one of their sons, Bubba or Richard, is always willing to visit and to talk about La Grange. The historic buildings in town reflect the early German and Czech settlers who were the Hrbaceks' predecessors.

The open-collar atmosphere of the restaurant makes relaxing and talking a pleasant way to spend time not needed for getting on your way. Some of the friendly waitresses have been with The Cottonwood for as long as thirty years, and they will also make you feel at home in this pleasant restaurant.

Serving hours: 6:30 a.m.–10:30 p.m. Monday through Thursday; 6
    a.m.–11:30 a.m. Sundays; 6:30 a.m.–midnight Friday and Saturday.
Closed: Christmas Eve, Christmas Day.
Breakfast, lunch, and dinner.
Cost of average meal: Moderate.

The Cottonwood Inn

State Hwy. 71 W.
La Grange
(512) 968-3646
Owners: V. A. and Jean
    Hrbacek

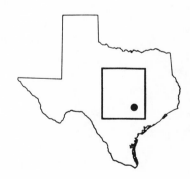

Credit cards accepted: American Express, Visa, MasterCard, Diners
    Club. No personal checks accepted.
Wheelchair accommodations: Front door and restrooms.
Reservations required for large parties.
Parking: Spacious.

The Settlement Inn

Boerne Stage Road Exit off I-10
Leon Springs
(512) 698-2580
Owner: Keith P. Miller

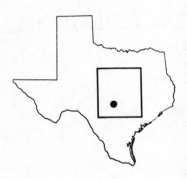

If you've been considering undertaking a quest for the best barbecue in the state, forget it. You'll only arrive at the inevitable conclu-
sion that among the best of good Texas barbecue, your choices are
going to be: "good," "better," and "Yee-hah!" Bring along a Texas Aggie to help you express the last, if you wish, because at The Settlement Inn, barbecue is all that's served.

Knowing how their barbecue gets to be the way it is won't matter to
you once you taste it, but nevertheless, the procedure is unique, even
for Texas. The best brisket available is pre-seasoned with a secret seasoning and smoked for over twenty hours in smoke from green live
oak. The meat never receives the direct heat of the fire. The ribs are
the most expensive that can be bought and are smoked in a very hot
fire for three hours as opposed to the slow, low heat of the brisket.
The pre-smoked beef and pork sausage are also the best available.

The Inn's special platter is an all-you-can-eat combination of ribs,
sausage, and beef served with green salad, spicy red beans, potato
salad, green onions, hot biscuits, and honey—all for $9.95 per per-
son, with half prices for children eight to twelve years old and for
diners sixty-five years and older. Also offered are a la carte plates with
somewhat similar portions. The combination plate of beef, sausage,
and ribs is enough for two moderate appetites.

The homemade cobbler is a mite expensive, but it is one of those
eating experiences that is hard to put a price on.

The setting for all this culinary bliss is worth the drive out from San
Antonio or the stop en route to the city from the north on I-10. You
can either eat inside the old rock building, which served as a general
store and post office, later a stage station in the 1800s, or outside under the oaks and elms, seated at big tables. Large groups are also
served inside the recently restored 1879 hotel across the patio. It is a
beautiful, rustic setting, and on warm nights the soft lighting outside
and the glow of kerosene lamps from the tables inside provide a place
to remember.

Serving hours: 5 p.m.–10 p.m. Monday through Thursday; 5 p.m.–11
    p.m. Friday and Saturday; 11:30 a.m.–10 p.m. Sunday.
Closed: Thanksgiving, December 24–26.
Lunch and dinner.
Cost of average meal: Expensive but children seven years and under
    free.
Half price meals for children eight to twelve years and for senior
    citizens.

Credit cards accepted: American Express, Visa, MasterCard, Carte
   Blanche, Diners Club. Personal checks by prior arrangement only as
   for large parties.
Special occasion services: Facilities for "any kind of bash." "We can
   arrange anything."
Wheelchair accommodations: Front door.
Reservations: For twenty or more only.
Parking: Spacious.

Anyone of a certain age and endowed with a romantic bent feels a
gentle stirring at the strains of the old song which begins "There's a
small hotel . . ." If this applies to you, the Badu House is your kind of
place, both an out-of-the-way inn and a restaurant, both guaranteed
to leave you with a peaceful contentment and a determination to return.

The classic building with the block shape of an Italian Renaissance
palace was built in 1891 as the First National Bank of Llano. In 1898 it
was purchased by N. J. Badu, a native of France, who lived in it with
his wife and two daughters until his death. In 1982, Earl and Ann
Ruff transformed it into the perfect setting for some of the best food
you will enjoy in this part of Texas.

Guests can have a drink in the Llanite Bar, so named after the beautiful polished mineral which covers the top of the bar and discovered
by "Prof." Badu north of Llano. Or they can eat in one of the three
dining rooms downstairs where they are surrounded by the ambi-
ence of the past: lace curtains, the original oak paneling, old photographs, patterned wallpaper, the patina of old furniture, the bank's
marble floors. Here and there, throughout the inn, women's hats
from another era are tossed on chairs and hang from wall hooks. Any
minute you expect someone in 1900's dress to descend the big staircase and enter the dining rooms.

The waitresses are dressed in fetching period costumes and the service is perfect. Midst all this elegant home-like atmosphere you can
enjoy one of Ann's many specialties, prepared by their treasured
cook, Angelita. Ann's jalapeño chicken shouldn't be missed—
chicken breasts wrapped in bacon, marinated in Italian dressing for
twenty-four hours, cooked with jalapeños and pimiento. Also try her
potatoes cooked in white wine. You won't forget her thin, cornbread
crepes, served hot along with the rolls.

Other menu choices include the sweet catfish. (You can be sure
Mississippi-born Ann insists on good catfish for her restaurant.)
Steaks and a beef kabob are also offered. The menu changes slightly
from day to day.

If you can bring yourself to leave after a meal, be sure at least to
look at the rooms upstairs where you can stay overnight if you wish.
Each room is furnished with antiques, many of which are from the
families of Earl and Ann. Each room is named after one of the Badu
family or a Ruff family member. With the room a continental breakfast is included. There are no televisions nor telephones (except in the

The Badu House

601 Bessemer at State Hwy. 71
Llano
(512) 247-4304
Owner: Ann Ruff

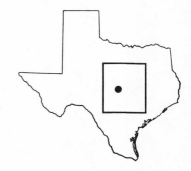

bar), no pets, and no room guests under fourteen. The Badu House is a peaceful and romantic spot to dine or spend a night.

Serving hours: 11:30 a.m.–2 p.m. Wednesday through Saturday; 6 p.m.–9 p.m. Wednesday through Thursday; 6 p.m.–10 p.m. Friday and Saturday; 12 p.m.–3 p.m. Sundays.
Closed: Monday, Tuesday, Sunday night.
Lunch and dinner.
Cost of average meal: Moderate.
Credit cards accepted: American Express, Visa, MasterCard, Diners Club, Carte Blanche. Personal checks accepted.
Special occasion services: Complete arrangements for any occasion.
Wheelchair accommodations: Front door and restrooms.
Reservations requested but not required.
Parking: Limited.

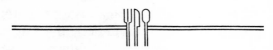

Kreuz Market

208 South Commerce, off the
courthouse square
Lockhart
(512) 398-2361
Owners: Edgar A. Schmidt and
Ricky Schmidt

"If a sausage maker gives you a recipe for good sausage, he's lyin'. It's not what you put in it; it's what you leave out." With those cryptic comments, Edgar Schmidt took me behind the scenes of his meat market and sausage factory, but all the preparation I saw of the smoked delicacies sold out front was the ladies tying the sausage casings. The less said about that the better, if you know the origin of those casings. The important thing is the post oak-smoked meat.

And meat is all you get, that is unless you pay extra for whole tomatoes, avocados, pickles, and sliced onions. At the counter next to the fragrant, blazing pit, you can purchase slices of brisket or whole sausage links, each one filled with the smoky goodness that Kreuz Market has been selling for over eighty years. You can pick up a soft drink or a beer at the counter inside the dining room at the same time you select the only side dishes available, which are the relishes. No potato salad, beans, nor slaw. And no silverware. There are plastic knives, and your plate is the brown butcher paper your meat is wrapped in. They call it "finger food" and furnish plenty of paper towels for napkins.

That's about all the atmosphere there is when you eat at the Kreuz Market (they pronounce it *kritz*), except for the high, pressed-tin ceiling in the old building and the lighted beer company signs along the walls. But you won't see anyone looking around for atmosphere. Everyone will be busy eating and licking their fingers and not worrying much about table manners.

Be sure to look at the 1924 dining area with its original wooden tables and benches. The Schmidts have even kept the old butcher knives, safely chained to each table.

Outside, you'll catch a glimpse of the Lockhart courthouse which looks as if it belongs on top of a cake. Around the corner is what the Schmidts call "the biggest woodpile in town," sometimes called an eyesore by some of the townspeople. Those folks must have problems with inhaling. One whiff of that post oak smoking the Schmidts' barbecue and who cares how big a woodpile is in the lot out back?

Serving hours: 7 a.m.–6 p.m. every day except Sunday.
Closed: Sundays, New Year's Day, July Fourth, Labor Day,
    Thanksgiving, Christmas Day.
Breakfast, lunch, and dinner.
Cost of average meal: Inexpensive.
No credit cards accepted. Some personal checks accepted.
Wheelchair accommodations: Front door and restrooms.
Parking: Spacious.
Beer only.

The Roper House

Let's hear a cheer for history-conscious people everywhere who save precious old structures, threatened by commercial opportunism. Don and Michelle Gunn saved the most significant building in their hometown of Marble Falls and converted it into one of the most beautiful restaurants in the state. There you will enjoy Southern cooking at its best or a wide range of other menu selections in the perfect setting for a relaxing meal.

The Roper Hotel was built in 1888 by George and Elizabeth Roper. Their photograph hangs at the top of the staircase, and you'll have fun guessing the reason behind the twinkle in George's eye. The dapper gentleman designed a sturdy building, made of locally manufactured brick. As one of the earliest hotels in this part of Texas, it served as a weekend stopover for Texas governors and politicians. It was also a stage stop and headquarters for drummers (traveling salesmen) of the time.

In 1978 Don and Michelle Gunn bought the Roper and transformed it into the jewel it is today. In the downstairs dining room, they have used blue patterned wallpaper above the white wainscoting (made from the laths found behind the plastered walls that were removed

*U.S. 281 at Third, three blocks
    from the river
Marble Falls
(512) 693-5561
Owners: Don and Michelle
    Gunn*

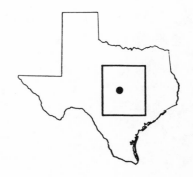

Roper House

throughout the hotel). Some of the walls are original, soft pink brick. Brass chandeliers, ceiling fans, antique furniture, and countless other details add up to create surroundings you won't want to leave. Upstairs, another beautiful dining room and a club are similarly decorated.

The menu features regional favorites such as chicken fried steak, fried okra, black-eyed peas, pinto beans, and cornbread. A marinated black-eyed pea salad should certainly be sampled. For real Southerners and Southwesterners there is cold buttermilk to drink.

You may prefer to order one of the Tex-Mex dishes or fried shrimp or perhaps a ribeye steak. It is all delicious. Each day five to seven different desserts are offered. Birthday celebrants can order the "Chocolate Lovers Delight," which is a special occasion in itself, made with brownies, vanilla ice cream, chocolate sauce, whipped cream, and a cherry.

After all of this good food and relaxation, you may want to sit a while in one of the rocking chairs on the upstairs porch. Or, if you've dined on the pretty terrace at the side of the Roper, look next door and you'll see the Gunns' Texas-type gift shop which they call the Lone Star.

Perhaps all of this is the reason for the twinkle in George Roper's eye. (How could he have known?)

Serving hours: 11 a.m.–10 p.m. Tuesday through Saturday; 10 a.m.–2 p.m. Sunday brunch buffet; 11 a.m.–9 p.m. Sundays a la carte.
Closed: Mondays, Christmas Day.
Lunch and dinner.
Cost of average meal: Moderate.
Credit cards accepted: American Express, Visa, MasterCard. Local personal checks accepted.
Special occasion services: "We encourage celebrations." Chocolate Lovers Delight.
Wheelchair accommodations: Front door.
Reservations: "Gladly accepted but not required."
Parking: Spacious.

During the 1870s, if H. D. Gruene hadn't had high hopes for cotton farming northwest of New Braunfels, there might never have been the little town of Gruene. Then, if the boll weevil and the Depression hadn't crushed those hopes, followed by more hopes and a lot of faith, Gruene wouldn't have been rescued from "ghost towndom" and wouldn't today be on the National Register of Historic Places.

In Gruene you'll never have to worry about bumping into a fast-food chain or service station, only a lovely cluster of time-burnished structures; the red brick Mercantile Building, Victorian houses, a rambling old dance hall in use again, craftsmen and shopowners quietly selling their wares in some of the old buildings, and the remains of the brick boiler house of Gruene's cotton gin, today transformed into the delightful Grist Mill Restaurant.

One look and you'll never doubt what an imaginative talent, in this case the talents of Chip Kaufman, can do with a building in ruins. Old timbers fill spaces around the old brick walls which were all that was left standing after the gin burned in 1922. You can sit inside and be cooled by breezes through the tall, open doorways and by overhead fans or sit outside on the deck overlooking the Guadalupe River. No more pleasant setting for a meal exists.

The menu offers a variety of fare, including steaks, chicken, and German sausage. One of their popular burgers is a "Wurstburger," featuring smoked sausage with barbecue sauce. Of course you don't have to order chicken fried steak, but if it isn't ordinarily your choice of entrees, try it just this once. Comparing chicken fried steaks in Texas is like comparing Texas skies on two separate summer days or two fields of spring wildflowers after a good rainy season. Within limits, there is no way. Let's just say that the Grist Mill's chicken fried steak is among the best you will have anywhere in the state. The crust is thick, the gravy a creamy, gold covering of luscious flavor. And the pinto beans . . . well, whatever seasonings they use give them the merest bite, make that a nip, not hot nor really spicy but hovering on the edge of hot and spicy. Unforgettable.

The Grist Mill Restaurant

North off FM 306 (Canyon Lake Exit) from I-35, left on Hunter
Gruene (New Braunfels)
(512) 625-0684
Owners: Patrick Molak and Mary Jane Nalley

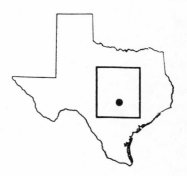

The strawberry shortcake they serve just might satisfy two or three hungry Cub Scouts. Perhaps that is a *slight* exaggeration. Anyway, it's big—and beautiful.

Beverages include beer, wines, hot or cold sangria, and mixed drinks.

Serving hours: 11:30 a.m.–10 p.m. Friday and Saturday, summer months; 11:30 a.m.–9 p.m. Tuesday and Thursday and Sunday, summer months.
Closed: Every Monday prior to Memorial Day and after Labor Day, mid-November to mid-March.
Lunch and dinner.
Cost of average meal: Lunch—inexpensive; dinner—moderate.
Credit cards accepted: American Express, Visa, MasterCard. Local checks accepted.
Special occasion services: Sing "Happy Birthday," help with surprise parties.
Wheelchair accommodations: Front door.
No reservations except for special parties.
Parking: Spacious.

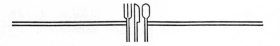

Krause's Cafe

148 S. Castell Ave., behind the Faust Hotel
New Braunfels
(512) 625-7581
Owners: Kermit and Mildred Krause

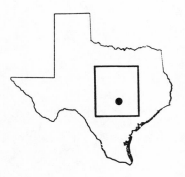

Breakfast at Krause's Cafe is a chatty gathering of local business and professional men, travelers, and the New Braunfels Lions Club, but the most interesting spot of all in the big, comfortable restaurant is the *stamptische* table. Here, each morning local dentists, ranchers, realtors, a preacher or two, and owner Kermit Krause assemble for breakfast, greeting each other by name and shaking hands around the table. Some who arrive take the places of those just getting up to leave for work. For several hours after the cafe opens, these friends drink coffee and eat breakfast, discussing mobile homes, fishing, and hunting trips in a pleasant blend of Texas and German accents. If you're a people-watcher, sit near this special table, and you'll see at once why Krause's has been in successful operation for over thirty-five years. Once you taste the food, you'll see again.

Mildred Krause instructs all her waitresses (and one outstanding waiter) to "treat every guest as special," and they do. If you're lucky, you'll be waited on by Ann Byrd with her over twelve years' experience at Krause's. Ann knows what good service is all about. She exchanges jokes with customers and pauses only to set down dishes between her tables and the kitchen. There she picks up plates of Krause's homemade sausage, peppered bacon, fist-sized biscuits, sliced tomatoes, and all the other Southern breakfast delicacies, including grits and hash-browns. You may envy the stamptische table a little. They get pint-sized jars of Kermit's preserves.

Noontime and dinner meals offer almost any German or Southern food you could want, all wonderful. The barbecue plate and barbecue dinner each offers a choice of meats: beef, sausage, chicken, ham and/or ribs; also a choice of vegetables and salad, including German potato salad, sauerkraut, and cole slaw (the latter would make the fast-food places that sell little cups of what they call cole slaw hang their heads in shame). Or you can order stewed ribs or pork hocks and sauerkraut, fried chicken, salmon croquettes, "sweet rice" (almost a pudding), creamed carrots, and other vegetables. Krause's also prepares steaks and burgers. During the winter months, Kermit makes a variety of sausages, available with other fresh meats in the market at the entrance. Menu items can be ordered to take out. Bottled and draft beer, both domestic and imported, are offered.

Name a kind of pie or cake and Krause's probably serves it: Black Forest, German chocolate, chocolate mint, Bavarian, walnut layer, carrot cream. Before you order your entree, you really should look over the dessert list, and be prepared for the servings in your single meal to be adequate for two moderate eaters.

Daughter Karen does much of the cooking, and Kermit and Mildred are easily found among their guests. Krause's reputation for good food and good service is easy to understand. You can watch them earn it every day.

Serving hours: 6:30 a.m.–8:30 p.m. Monday through Saturday.
Closed: Sundays, New Year's Day, July Fourth, Labor Day,
    Thanksgiving, Christmas Eve, Christmas Day.
Breakfast, lunch, and dinner.
Cost of average meal: Breakfast and lunch—inexpensive;
    dinner—moderate.
No credit cards accepted. Personal checks accepted.
Special occasion services: Cake if given sufficient notice.
Wheelchair accommodations: Front door.
Parking: Spacious.

Wolfgang's Keller

*295 E. San Antonio, in the
    Prince Solms Inn
New Braunfels
(512) 625-9169
Owner: Bill Knight*

If you have ever been inside the Prince Solms Inn, you know all about the romantic surroundings: the elegant antiques, the attention to details such as only quality magazines strewn here and there in the parlor. In Wolfgang's Keller under the inn, you'll enjoy the same atmosphere. Lighting is soft, almost dim. Exposed brick and wood-paneled walls provide the perfect setting for period furniture and fine art pieces. And owner Bill Knight's music from his baby grand piano is exceptionally good "music of your life."

The downstairs restaurant is relatively new, but nothing is missing in quality or service. Bill came to New Braunfels from Houston, but he learned how to prepare one of his best appetizers from a friend in San Antonio. His "Vietnamese Spring Rolls" are light-as-air-type egg rolls, filled with truly fresh garden vegetables from the garden behind the inn.

Entrees include "Shrimp Dijon," "Veal Marsala," steaks, and red snapper. According to Bill, the "Chicken Picata," billed as "George Washington's favorite dish" has been authenticated by *Houston Post*

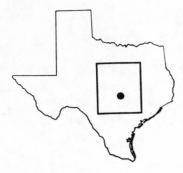

columnist Marge Crumbaker. George certainly appreciated good food, if this is an example—a delicately sauteed chicken breast in butter and olive oil, topped with imported Spanish Madeira wine, served over brown rice. The fresh broccoli accompanying it made us vow never never again to cook any from a frozen package. Such are the consequences of eating the best.

The dinner salad included fresh mushrooms with a delicious house vinaigrette dressing. A house bleu cheese dressing is also offered.

In this part of Texas, the renowned Blue Bell ice cream is available almost everywhere, and if you have never tasted it, by all means, do. At Wolfgang's it is on the dessert list and also teamed with some exotic after-dinner drinks. "Frangelico Freeze," "Amaretto Freeze," and "Velvet Hammer" may also be ordered without ice cream, but go all the way. You only live once.

If this early direction continues, Wolfgang's Keller can go nowhere but ahead as one of the outstanding small restaurants in the state. While in New Braunfels, don't miss it.

Serving hours: 5 p.m.–11 p.m. every day except Monday.
Closed: Mondays, Christmas Eve.
Dinner only.
Cost of average meal: Expensive.
Credit cards accepted: Visa, MasterCard. Personal checks accepted.
Special occasion services: Petits Fours and candle for birthday,
    anniversary.
Wheelchair accommodations: Stairs down.
Special dress required: Casual to dressy.
Reservations: Suggested.
Parking: Spacious.

Pontotoc Inn

U.S. Hwy. 71
Pontotoc (23 miles west of
    Llano)
(512) 251-6667
Owners: Lewis and Betty
    Waldon

From Brady to Llano the road dips and winds through the northern edge of the Texas Hill Country, carpeted with wild flowers in the spring, lonely and townless. Then there is Pontotoc, population about fifty. You'll have no trouble locating the Pontotoc Inn or Cafe (signs call it both). Across the way from the stone ruins of San Fernando Academy and the general store, the cafe and post office share the same small building. Here Pontotockians drift into the post office, then into the cafe for some of Betty Waldon's good country cooking or just to visit with neighbors. Betty is also Pontotoc's postmaster.

In the best sense, the surroundings and the menu are simple, and the only thing which is quick or hurried is the service. If your muscles are all kinked up from driving, you can slide into one of the comfortable booths and relax while you wait briefly for your order. No blinking TV screen, no background music, no rattling dishes, just low, easy conversation among townsfolk.

The Pontotoc Inn isn't an inn but a combined post office and cafe where townsfolk gather for friendly talk and good home cooking.

On Mondays, only lunch is served, and it is pure Texana: pinto beans, cornbread and peach cobbler. Other days you can have one of Betty's catfish dinners or maybe chicken fried steak. A king-size CFS should hold you at least until you get to Austin or further down the road. Betty believes in never cutting costs on meat, so you can be sure it's the best she can get.

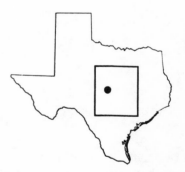

The menu also offers steaks, quail, shrimp, Mexican food, hot and cold sandwiches, and a wide selection of special plates for children. Homemade desserts include peach cobbler, apple and chocolate pies, and strawberry shortcake.

While you enjoy your meal, you may hear diners discussing the annual Pontotoc Ranch Fire Association benefit barbecue held each September. Or Alvin Turner from down in Bonham may drop in with some of the handcrafts he creates. You may be the only stranger there, but you'll feel right at home. It's that kind of small-town-friendly place.

Serving hours: 11 a.m.–8:30 p.m. Wednesday through Saturday; 12 p.m.–2 p.m. Mondays.

Closed: Sunday, Tuesday, New Year's Day, Labor Day, Thanksgiving, Christmas Day.

Lunch, dinner, and afternoon snacks.

Cost of average meal: Inexpensive.

Special plates for children, dieters or senior citizens; chicken strips with gravy, chef salad, fruit plate with chicken salad.

No credit cards accepted. Personal checks accepted.

Wheelchair accommodations: Front door.

Parking: Spacious.

No alcohol served.

The Alpine Cottage

1103 Wonder Drive off I-35
Round Rock
(512) 255-0517
Owners: Billy and Johanna
*   Maddox*

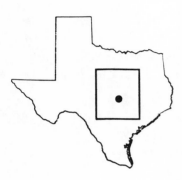

If you go on a Thursday, Friday, or Saturday night, you may walk in on the weekly singalong, led by piano player/tenor Bill Owens, playing and directing with a full beer mug. Owner Johanna may even be leading some of her guests through the lively steps of "The Chicken Dance." Anyone not singing "Michael, Row the Boat Ashore" or "Beer Barrel Polka" from the songbooks at each table will probably be eating. Or listening to gregarious Johanna explain in her German-flavored speech just how she prepares the recipes she brought with her from Munich.

Her rye bread is chewy and delicious. Wafer-thin veal (weiner schnitzel) comes covered in a light, bread crumb crust. Johanna assures you she makes her own bread crumbs. "Beef Roluden" is a stuffed, German dill pickle although it doesn't look like one. This savory dish is accompanied by a potato dumpling and red cabbage. She is proud, as she deserved to be, of her "Eisbein (cured ham hock) with Sauerkraut and Potato Salad" entree. Or you can have one of three German sausages: knockwurst, bratwurst, or weiswurst.

Dessert might be cheese and/or apple strudel with ice cream. The strudel will be hot and *wunderbar*!

This is not the restaurant for the unsociable. If you like friendly people and lots of conviviality, this place has it all. Johanna will invite you to sit with her and her friends at the "house table" if you look lonely. Maybe even if you don't. If it's your birthday, she'll put a can-

Authentic German food and a lively atmosphere are the attractions at The Alpine Cottage.

dle in your apple strudel and Bill will play your special song whether it's "Happy Birthday" or "Danny Boy." Ask him to play and sing "Danny Boy" anyway. It will positively send shivers down your arms.

You won't want to leave, but when you do, Johanna will urge you to come back. She'll tell you, "The happiness of the people is what I want." She means it, and at the Alpine Cottage, there is a lot of it always around.

Serving hours: 11 a.m.–2 p.m., 5:30 p.m. until everyone has to go
   home.
Closed: New Year's Day, Easter, Memorial Day, July Fourth, Labor Day,
   Thanksgiving, Christmas Day.
Lunch and dinner.
Cost of average meal: Moderate.
Credit cards accepted: Visa, MasterCard. No personal checks accepted.
Wheelchair accommodations: Front door.
Special required dress: shirt, shoes.
Reservations requested.
Parking: Spacious.

Katy Station Restaurant and Bar

Corner of Cheatam and C. M. Allen Pkwy.
San Marcos
(512) 396-5010
Owners: Ted and Sue Cohen, John Thompson

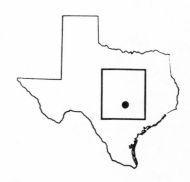

Even if you aren't old enough to remember waiting for a train in a depot, and especially if you are, you'll love the nostalgic feel of Katy Station. Built in the 1890s, the building served as the Missouri, Kansas, Texas (Katy) freight and passenger depot for San Marcos until March of 1980 when it was moved to its present location. In the bar you can see grafitti left by idle freight handlers. The middle dining room once housed the ticket, baggage, and Western Union offices, and the other two dining rooms served as segregated waiting rooms.

On the walls hang photographs and railroad advertisements from the depot's early days, including one touting dining car meals: "Breakfast—30¢, Lunch—35¢, Dinner—40¢." Katy Station's prices today are equally appropriate for the 1980s.

Menu choices are listed with fitting railroad names, but the most non-railroad and appealing name is the first appetizer, called simply "Fried Things." That's stating it plainly enough without actually describing the tasty, batter-fried muschrooms, squash, and onion rings, served with homemade gravy. Then there are the "Station-Master Specialties" which include, of course, chicken fried steak and other chicken and steak selections. A favorite among San Marcos diners is the "Chicken Oscar," a juicy grilled breast of chicken on a bed of rice, topped with asparagus spears and "smothered in hollandaise sauce." Served only when the freshest seafood is available, the "Ocean Freight" items include oysters on the half-shell, shrimp scampi, fried shrimp, and a redfish almondine.

Not all restaurants offer appealing menus for children, but at Katy Station, young guests can choose from a fried shrimp plate with french fries and green beans or fried chicken fingers with gravy, green beans, and french fries, or a hamburger steak accompanied by green beans and french fries.

"End of the Line" desserts feature a buttermilk pie described as "Mom's Favorite Recipe." You'll love Mom for sharing it with Katy Station.

The Tank Car offers several creative drinks, including "Texas Tea," unlike any Don Meredith ever promoted on TV. The Tank Car bartender makes it with equal parts of gin, vodka, rum, and tequila with a sweet and sour mix, a splash of coke, and a lime squeeze. You might want to try one of the ice cream drinks, a Brandy Alexander, Kahlua Freeze, or Golden Cadillac. Two of their winter specialties are Jamaican coffee and hot buttered rum. A large selection of beers is available as well as wines and champagnes. Five days a week the bar features live entertainment.

Service is swift, and the attractive college student waitresses from Southwest Texas State University in San Marcos are attentive and efficient.

Serving hours: 11:30 a.m.–2:30 p.m. (lunch), 5 p.m.–10 p.m. daily.
Closed: Lunch between Labor Day and Easter, Thanksgiving, Christmas Day.
Lunch and dinner.
Cost of average meal: Inexpensive to moderate.
Credit cards accepted: American Express, Visa, MasterCard. Local checks accepted.
Special occasion services: Cheesecake with candle, singing waiters.
Wheelchair accommodations: Front door.
Reservations: Suggested for large parties.
Parking: Spacious.

When *Texas Highways* magazine ran an article on some of the best chicken fried steak in the state, they probably weren't prepared for the response they got. Not that their readers disagreed with their examples, but dozens of CFS lovers had their own nominees. So many that the magazine ran a follow-up story, printing just a few of the flood of letters they received. One Temple resident declared what hundreds of Templeites have known for thirty-five years: the *best* chicken fried steak is served at the Bluebonnet Restaurant.

At this unpretentious but friendly little restaurant across the street from the old Santa Fe Hospital, the chicken fried steak is served on a separate plate and the crust is thick and crispy-tender, the gravy golden and flavorsome. As in many other Texas restaurants, it is the most frequently ordered item on the menu.

Other entrees include just about anything a diner with a southern or southwestern palate could want: fried chicken, Mexican plates, roast beef, steak, fish (oysters, catfish, trout, etc.) pork chops, sandwiches, and salads, even special plates for children and half orders for children or senior citizens.

In the kitchen one cook has been with the restaurant for twenty-five years, and such experience shows in the seasoning of the vegetables; yellow wax beans, glazed beets, candied carrots, baked squash, pinto beans, and much more. Each day's special includes a meat, three vegetables, a salad, hot rolls and cornbread, a drink, and a dessert, all for an astoundingly modest price. The pies are all fantastic as are the bread pudding and rice pudding. In fact, everything the Bluebonnet serves is southern cooking at its best.

The other diners will be mostly nice-looking Temple residents, the kind of people in whom Texans take pride. But perhaps the most pleasant part of eating at the Bluebonnet is observing the family pride and attention shown by the owners. Laverne Pitts ran the restaurant for thirty-five years with her late husband, whom she credits for the

Bluebonnet Restaurant

705 S. 25th St., off I-35 at 57th St. Exit, left on H St.
Temple
(817) 773-6654
Owners: Laverne Pitts, George and Susan Luck

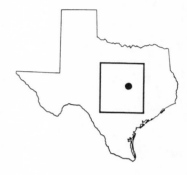

Many Texans claim The Bluebonnet Restaurant in Temple serves the best chicken fried steak anywhere.

tradition of good service and caring about their guests. She is the same sort of restaurateur, as is son-in-law George Luck. They constantly check on the service and the guests' satisfaction with their meals, with Laverne excusing herself to check on a tardy order or stopping to hug a small grandchild who has dropped in and George visiting with local businessmen sitting at the counter. It is a neighborly kind of place where strangers feel as if they have been there before.

During April or May, you will find fresh bluebonnets on the tables, an annual gift from a friend who grows them on his nearby farm. Some of the customers are enjoying them as fourth generation diners. The flower is an appropriate symbol of a small, hometown restaurant where family pride reflects the best in Texas hospitality.

Serving hours: 5 a.m.–9 p.m. Monday through Wednesday, Friday through Sunday.
Closed: Thursdays, New Year's Day, Easter, Mother's Day, Memorial Day, July Fourth, Labor Day, Thanksgiving, Christmas Eve, Christmas Day.
Breakfast, lunch, and dinner.
Cost of average meal: Inexpensive.
No credit cards accepted. Local checks accepted.
Special occasion services: Homemade sweet roll with a candle.
Wheelchair accommodations: Front door.
Special required dress: Gentlemen will be asked to remove their hats.
Parking: Spacious.
No alcohol served.

The Lone Star Tavern

U.S. 84 E., off Loop 340,
*   Bellmead Dr. Exit*
Waco
(817) 799-0918 or 799-0027
Other location: 3730 Franklin,
*   (817) 753-0825*
Owner: Ida Buck

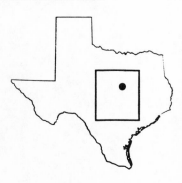

Hungry for steak, some visiting businessmen asked the motel coffee shop waitress where to find the best steak in Waco. She said, "The Lone Star Tavern." Then they asked the desk clerk. He said, "The Lone Star Tavern." Still unpersuaded, they turned to the Yellow Pages and saw where someone had circled the LST ad in red and written, "Go no further. You've found it!" This is the consensus of the hundreds of devotees of the original restaurant just north of Waco.

It isn't a tavern, although it was in the beginning, and looks like it from the outside. Inside it does too. Pure Texas honky tonk decor. But it's the ideal setting for the reason people flock there—steaks. Almost nothing but steaks. And potatoes. Huge and baked or french fried and receiving as much pre-cooking attention as the steaks. All the meat is fresh, nothing is ever frozen, and every steak is cut and trimmed to perfection. The fries are first soaked in ice water to reduce the starch, then blanched, refrigerated, and finally fried. They're big and tender and make fast food fries unworthy of being called potatoes. You do get a small salad, but if you want frills like another vegetable or dessert, you'll have to go somewhere else. The only other "extra" is plain white, sliced bread. Not even rolls or cornbread.

Country honky tonk inside and out, the Lone Star Tavern is a no-frills place in both decor and menu with a well-deserved reputation for fabulous steaks.

Then there is the chicken fried steak and gravy. You think you've tasted cream gravy? Sure, you can make it the usual way with pan drippings, and there are plenty in the Lone Star's kitchen, but here they use pure butter as a base. Baylor law students celebrate graduation here and tell owner Ida Buck, "We never would have made it without your chicken fried steak."

Ida says she's the only restaurant owner she has ever heard of who enlarged her waiting room rather than her dining room to accommodate the crowds. A Dallas church regularly brings an entire busload of their members to Waco to enjoy Lone Star steaks.

The steaks are cooked by the original owner, Charlie Mueller. He beams with pride when he talks about his steaks and how they are cooked. Charlie is a former Army cook, but he gives that position a new reputation.

Ida is an entrepreneur of apparent limitless ideas and energy. Her Italian heritage gives her the look of a lady who might be seen in a TV commercial, promoting her spaghetti sauce. She even tried serving spaghetti at the Lone Star, but she says people only wanted her steaks.

The same food is served at the Franklin Street restaurant in Waco, but a lot of her regulars prefer the Lone Star. Those businessmen who were finally convinced they should "go no further" surely do. When they had finished their steaks, Ida insisted on driving them back to their motel.

Serving hours: 11 a.m.–9:30 p.m. Monday through Saturday.
Closed: Sundays, New Year's Day, Thanksgiving, Christmas Eve,
    Christmas Day.
Lunch and dinner.
Cost of average meal: Moderate.
Credit cards accepted: Visa and MasterCard. Personal checks accepted.
Special occasion services: Dish of wrapped candy with candle, "Happy
    Birthday" sung by waitresses.
Wheelchair accommodations: Front door and restrooms.
Parking: Spacious.

Nick's

*4508 Waco Drive, off Valley
    Mills Drive*
Waco
(817) 772-7790
*Owners: Nick Klaras, Evan
    Klaras*

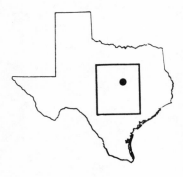

The ancient Greeks believed fiercely in the goal of excellence. At Nick's, Nick Klaras and his son Evan are carrying on that tradition with their fine Greek and American foods, along with good service and a quiet, attractive setting.

Nick's father, Pete Klaras, began the family restaurateur line with a restaurant in Waco back in 1904. Nick is a graduate of Baylor University, as is son Evan, but both trained for other careers. However, tradition runs deep in Greek-American families. Nick has owned the restaurant for over twenty-five years. One visit, and you'll agree that their devotion to excellence shows in every aspect of their business.

Of course you don't have to order Greek food, but if you already enjoy it or if you have never tasted it, either is reason enough for ordering what will be some of the best you will have anywhere. Your first sampling may be, along with homemade bread sticks, Greek paximathia, which are little seed-filled cookies. One light entree is tiropita, paper-thin layers of buttered pastry (fillo) filled with a mixture of marvelous Greek cheeses. This is served with a salad and a vegetable. The house dressing for salads is creamy and made with feta cheese.

Other Greek entrees include souvlakia, succulent tenderloin tips, marinated in wine and herbs, then skewered with fresh vegetables and broiled. Some Greek restaurants use lamb in their meat dishes, but Nick says experience has shown there is little demand for lamb in this part of the state. Moussaka is a favorite of Greek food lovers. It is prepared with lean ground beef, potatoes, and eggplant, covered with a light cheese sauce, then baked. If you really like Greek food, you'll enjoy dolmathes, cabbage or grape leaves (ask for whichever you prefer), stuffed with a blend of beef, rice, and herbs, and topped with a creamy lemon-butter sauce. You can also have broiled seafood, prepared Greek style or a large Greek salad containing the wonderful Kalamata black olives and feta cheese.

If you're the only one in your party who soars to Olympian rapture over Greek cuisine, try to talk the others into at least trying baklava for dessert. They will bless you. At Nick's the airy fillo pastry is layered with crushed pecans, smothered in a sauce of honey, orange, and lemon rind, and studded with a clove. This Bacchanalian confection will better help anyone to understand the meaning of "food of the gods."

If Greek food doesn't appeal to you, Nick's serves a wide selection of beef and chicken dishes, hot and cold sandwiches, and seafood. Luncheon favorites include chicken fried steak, smoked Polish sausage, fried catfish filets, and an executive special plate for the calorie-watching executive. The dinner menu expands the seafood selections with almost any fish you could want. Incidentally, among the drinks available are several good Greek wines.

If you've been a traveler to Greece or you remember your Greek mythology, you'll appreciate the decor of the Labyrinth Club in the restaurant. An interesting frieze, made by the Klaras family, is behind the bar, depicting symbols from King Minos' palace on the island of Crete.

Nick's does a lot of local catering, and the family are loyal Baylor supporters. One wall is covered with photos of Baylor football players and two from other schools ("good friends", Nick says). This hospitable restaurateur will happily discuss football, jazz, Greek food, or any other topic. Nick's is a Waco restaurant you shouldn't miss.

Serving hours: 11 a.m.–9:30 p.m. Monday through Thursday; 11
   a.m.–10 p.m. Friday; 5 p.m.–10 p.m. Saturday.
Closed: Sundays, New Year's Day, Memorial Day, July Fourth,
   Labor Day, Thanksgiving, December 24 through January 1.
Lunch and dinner.
Cost of average meal: Inexpensive to expensive.
Credit cards accepted: American Express, Visa, MasterCard, Diners
   Club, Carte Blanche. Personal checks for amount of meal only.
Special occasion services: Complimentary cake with two to three hours'
   notice.
Wheelchair accommodations: Front door.
Special required dress: "Neatly dressed. No hats worn inside."
Parking: Spacious.

The Water Works

Lake Brazos Drive at Mill
Waco
(817) 756-2181
Owner: Geoffrey Michael

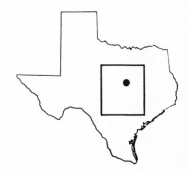

Try to have some time to spare when you eat at the Water Works. Not because the service is lacking, because it is fast and flawless! But you'll want to take in the setting inside this 1914 Waco Water Works building. Even if you're too young to remember the Mobil Oil Company's flying red horse logo or the Voice of Firestone, you'll still enjoy and appreciate the restaurant's "nostalgic elegance" as owner-chef Geoffrey Michael calls it.

If you want an intimate nook for your lunch or dinner, you have your choices of a booth lighted by a crystal chandelier, a cozy corner framed in Victorian gingerbread, a booth with an old brass bed seat back under antique stained glass church windows, or even the interior of an old MKT boxcar, thoughtfully and softly lighted as is the entire restaurant.

The Pump Station Bar contains more interesting reminders of the past and features live entertainment from Dallas, New Orleans, or Waco, Tuesday through Saturday. There is room for dancing, too. The bartender makes a stout margarita, and the menu lists a good selection of wines and champagnes.

There may be equally good food as beautifully prepared and served *somewhere* else in the world, say on the Orient Express, but the matter is debatable. Geoffrey Michael has an impressive background in culinary training and experience, beginning with the Plaza Hotel in New York City at the age of eighteen. His self-admitted workaholic nature and a devotion to his craft produces some of the most elegant dishes you will find anywhere. If he has the time, he will happily prepare almost anything you request, but anything on his menu is bound to be one of the most memorable meals you will ever enjoy. His "Shrimp Gabrielle" is a "mysterious blend of spices, herbs, and wine, simmered with jacketed Gulf shrimp." This is an appetizer cov-

In The Water Works everything is a conversation piece, including brass bed seats, an old MKT boxcar, stained glass windows—and the food.

ered with the salty, zesty sauce he created. The blend is now being marketed under the name "Gabrielle" seasoned salt. One of his entrees is "Mignonettes of Beef Oscar," which is tenderloin of beef with sauteed King Crab, asparagus, and mushrooms, topped with Bearnaise sauce. The flounder almondine is exquisite and begs for a foods photographer, it is so picture-perfect.

There are other fish selections, chicken, and steaks. A favorite veal dish of returning diners, and there must be hundreds, is "Cotoletta Milanese," a veal cutlet covered with grated Romano cheese and drenched in brown butter. Baked zucchini covered with Swiss and Romano cheese is an unforgettable side dish.

The dessert list is called "O Why Not", and you'll agree. Try the "Strawberries Chantilly" or the "New Orleans Mile High Pie" with kahlua sauce.

You'll probably hear a lot of "Happy Birthday" singing upstairs or off in a corner because this is the kind of place to celebrate something—or nothing at all. Just eating at the Water Works is a celebration in itself.

Serving hours: 11 a.m.–2 p.m., 5 p.m.–10 p.m. Tuesday through Friday;
   5 p.m.–10:30 p.m. Saturday; 11 a.m.–2 p.m., 5 p.m.–9 p.m. Sunday.
Closed: Mondays, New Year's Day, July Fourth, Thanksgiving,
   Christmas Day.
Lunch and dinner.
Cost of average meal: Expensive.
Credit cards accepted: American Express, Visa, Diners Club.
No personal checks accepted.
Special occasion services: Ice cream cake on the menu meals.
Wheelchair accommodations: Front steps but assistance given.
   Restrooms with help.
Parking: Spacious.

Food Directory

The following lists major types of food served in the great hometown restaurants in this book. Some restaurants are listed in more than one category. Many restaurants serve a sprinkling of several kinds of food (practically every restaurant in Texas serves chicken fried steak). These listings represent some of the best.

Index